MEMORABLE DAT

Notes pocket

Celebrating 40 years

1982 – 2022

Throughout the history of the Dairy Diary, it has remained true to its roots and still sells via the milkman.

It's now 40 years old and has an extremely loyal following, with many purchasers owning the full set of diaries, dating back to the early eighties.

Thank you for supporting us.

Dairy Diary 2022

Name
....

Address
....

....

Postcode
....

☎ Home
....

☎ Mobile
....

Email
....

....

In case of emergency contact:
....

Name
....

☎ Tel.
....

DairyDiary.co.uk

 @DairyDiary   @OriginalDairyDiary

To order: 0344 4725265

PLANNER 2022

JANUARY		FEBRUARY	MARCH	
1	Sat	1 Tue	1 Tue	
2	Sun	2 Wed	2 Wed	
3	Mon	BANK HOLIDAY UK	3 Thu	3 Thu
4	Tue	BANK HOLIDAY SCOTLAND	4 Fri	4 Fri
5	Wed	5 Sat	5 Sat	
6	Thu	6 Sun	6 Sun	
7	Fri	7 Mon	7 Mon	
8	Sat	8 Tue	8 Tue	
9	Sun	9 Wed	9 Wed	
10	Mon	10 Thu	10 Thu	
11	Tue	11 Fri	11 Fri	
12	Wed	12 Sat	12 Sat	
13	Thu	13 Sun	13 Sun	
14	Fri	14 Mon	14 Mon	
15	Sat	15 Tue	15 Tue	
16	Sun	16 Wed	16 Wed	
17	Mon	17 Thu	17 Thu	BANK HOLIDAY N. IRELAND
18	Tue	18 Fri	18 Fri	
19	Wed	19 Sat	19 Sat	
20	Thu	20 Sun	20 Sun	
21	Fri	21 Mon	21 Mon	
22	Sat	22 Tue	22 Tue	
23	Sun	23 Wed	23 Wed	
24	Mon	24 Thu	24 Thu	
25	Tue	25 Fri	25 Fri	
26	Wed	26 Sat	26 Sat	
27	Thu	27 Sun	27 Sun	
28	Fri	28 Mon	28 Mon	
29	Sat		29 Tue	
30	Sun		30 Wed	
31	Mon		31 Thu	

APRIL	MAY	JUNE
1 Fri	**1 Sun**	1 Wed
2 Sat	2 Mon BANK HOLIDAY UK	2 Thu BANK HOLIDAY UK
3 Sun	3 Tue	3 Fri BANK HOLIDAY UK
4 Mon	4 Wed	**4 Sat**
5 Tue	5 Thu	**5 Sun**
6 Wed	6 Fri	6 Mon
7 Thu	**7 Sat**	7 Tue
8 Fri	**8 Sun**	8 Wed
9 Sat	9 Mon	9 Thu
10 Sun	10 Tue	10 Fri
11 Mon	11 Wed	**11 Sat**
12 Tue	12 Thu	**12 Sun**
13 Wed	13 Fri	13 Mon
14 Thu	**14 Sat**	14 Tue
15 Fri BANK HOLIDAY UK	**15 Sun**	15 Wed
16 Sat	16 Mon	16 Thu
17 Sun	17 Tue	17 Fri
18 Mon BANK HOLIDAY UK (EXCL. SCOTLAND)	18 Wed	**18 Sat**
19 Tue	19 Thu	**19 Sun**
20 Wed	20 Fri	20 Mon
21 Thu	**21 Sat**	21 Tue
22 Fri	**22 Sun**	22 Wed
23 Sat	23 Mon	23 Thu
24 Sun	24 Tue	24 Fri
25 Mon	25 Wed	**25 Sat**
26 Tue	26 Thu	**26 Sun**
27 Wed	27 Fri	27 Mon
28 Thu	**28 Sat**	28 Tue
29 Fri	**29 Sun**	29 Wed
30 Sat	30 Mon	30 Thu
	31 Tue	P.T.O. July–December 2022

PLANNER 2022

JULY	AUGUST	SEPTEMBER
1 Fri	1 Mon BANK HOLIDAY SCOTLAND	1 Thu
2 Sat	2 Tue	2 Fri
3 Sun	3 Wed	**3 Sat**
4 Mon	4 Thu	**4 Sun**
5 Tue	5 Fri	5 Mon
6 Wed	**6 Sat**	6 Tue
7 Thu	**7 Sun**	7 Wed
8 Fri	8 Mon	8 Thu
9 Sat	9 Tue	9 Fri
10 Sun	10 Wed	**10 Sat**
11 Mon	11 Thu	**11 Sun**
12 Tue BANK HOLIDAY N. IRELAND	12 Fri	12 Mon
13 Wed	**13 Sat**	13 Tue
14 Thu	**14 Sun**	14 Wed
15 Fri	15 Mon	15 Thu
16 Sat	16 Tue	16 Fri
17 Sun	17 Wed	**17 Sat**
18 Mon	18 Thu	**18 Sun**
19 Tue	19 Fri	19 Mon
20 Wed	**20 Sat**	20 Tue
21 Thu	**21 Sun**	21 Wed
22 Fri	22 Mon	22 Thu
23 Sat	23 Tue	23 Fri
24 Sun	24 Wed	**24 Sat**
25 Mon	25 Thu	**25 Sun**
26 Tue	26 Fri	26 Mon
27 Wed	**27 Sat**	27 Tue
28 Thu	**28 Sun**	28 Wed
29 Fri	29 Mon BANK HOLIDAY UK (EXCL. SCOTLAND)	29 Thu
30 Sat	30 Tue	30 Fri
31 Sun	31 Wed	

OCTOBER	NOVEMBER	DECEMBER
1 Sat	1 Tue	1 Thu
2 Sun	2 Wed	2 Fri
3 Mon	3 Thu	**3 Sat**
4 Tue	4 Fri	**4 Sun**
5 Wed	**5 Sat**	5 Mon
6 Thu	**6 Sun**	6 Tue
7 Fri	7 Mon	7 Wed
8 Sat	8 Tue	8 Thu
9 Sun	9 Wed	9 Fri
10 Mon	10 Thu	**10 Sat**
11 Tue	11 Fri	**11 Sun**
12 Wed	**12 Sat**	12 Mon
13 Thu	**13 Sun**	13 Tue
14 Fri	14 Mon	14 Wed
15 Sat	15 Tue	15 Thu
16 Sun	16 Wed	16 Fri
17 Mon	17 Thu	**17 Sat**
18 Tue	18 Fri	**18 Sun**
19 Wed	**19 Sat**	19 Mon
20 Thu	**20 Sun**	20 Tue
21 Fri	21 Mon	21 Wed
22 Sat	22 Tue	22 Thu
23 Sun	23 Wed	23 Fri
24 Mon	24 Thu	**24 Sat**
25 Tue	25 Fri	**25 Sun**
26 Wed	**26 Sat**	26 Mon BANK HOLIDAY UK
27 Thu	**27 Sun**	27 Tue BANK HOLIDAY UK
28 Fri	28 Mon	28 Wed
29 Sat	29 Tue	29 Thu
30 Sun	30 Wed	30 Fri
31 Mon		**31 Sat**

Contents

A 'Could Do' list for 2022 26

Say yes to yoga 30

Why helping others is healthy 32

USEFUL REMINDERS

PERSONAL

Bank

Beauty therapist

Building society

Citizen's Advice   citizensadvice.org.uk

   for England   03444 111 444

   for Wales   03444 77 20 20

Credit card emergency 1

Credit card emergency 2

Hairdresser

Life insurance policy number

   ☎ contact

   renewal date

Samaritans   116 123 (or local branch)

             samaritans.org

Solicitor

Work

HEALTH

Blood group

Chemist

Chiropodist

Dentist

Doctor

Hospital

Medical insurance policy number

   ☎ contact

   renewal date

National insurance number

NHS (non-emergency)   111   nhs.uk

NHS number

Optician

Notes

HOME

Boiler service date

Childminder/nursery

Council

Electrician

Electricity provider

Gas engineer

Gas provider

Home insurance policy number

☎ contact

renewal date

Plumber

Police (non-emergency)   101   police.uk

School

TV licence renewal date

Vet

Water provider

TRAVEL

Car insurance policy number

☎ contact

renewal date

Breakdown service

Driving licence number

Garage

MOT due date

Road tax renewal date

Service date

Vehicle registration number

Eurostar   03432 186 186   eurostar.com

National Rail enq.   0345 748 4950

nationalrail.co.uk

Taxi

Passport adviceline   0300 222 0000

gov.uk/passport-advice-line

Passport number

renewal date

EHIC/GHIC number

renewal date

Travel agent

Travel insurance policy number

☎ contact

renewal date

FAMILY & FRIENDS

Name

Address

☎ Home

Work

Mobile

Email

Name

Address

☎ Home

Work

Mobile

Email

Name

Address

☎ Home

Work

Mobile

Email

Name

Address

☎ Home

Work

Mobile

Email

Name

Address

☎ Home

Work

Mobile

Email

Name

Address

☎ Home

Work

Mobile

Email

Name

Address

☎ Home

Work

Mobile

Email

Name

Address

☎ Home

Work

Mobile

Email

Name

Address

☎ Home

Work

Mobile

Email

Name

Address

☎ Home

Work

Mobile

Email

Name

Address

☎ Home

Work

Mobile

Email

Name

Address

☎ Home

Work

Mobile

Email

FAMILY & FRIENDS

Name

Address

Home

Work

Mobile

Email

Name

Address

Home

Work

Mobile

Email

Name

Address

Home

Work

Mobile

Email

Name

Address

Home

Work

Mobile

Email

Name

Address

Home

Work

Mobile

Email

Name

Address

Home

Work

Mobile

Email

Name

Address

☎ Home

Work

Mobile

Email

Name

Address

☎ Home

Work

Mobile

Email

Name

Address

☎ Home

Work

Mobile

Email

Name

Address

☎ Home

Work

Mobile

Email

Name

Address

☎ Home

Work

Mobile

Email

Name

Address

☎ Home

Work

Mobile

Email

HOME BUDGETING

	JANUARY	FEBRUARY	MARCH
Opening balance			
Income			
New balance			
Birthdays/Christmas			
Car insurance			
Car MOT/service/tax			
Childcare			
Clothing/shoes			
Council tax			
Dentist/optician			
Electricity			
Entertainment			
Gas/oil/solid fuel			
Groceries			
Hairdresser			
Holidays			
Home/pet insurance			
Life/medical insurance			
Mobile/phone/internet			
Mortgage/rent			
Newspapers/magazines			
Petrol/fares			
Pets			
Savings			
Subscriptions			
TV licence/satellite			
Water			
Total expenditure			
Closing balance			

HOME BUDGETING

	APRIL	MAY	JUNE
Opening balance			
Income			
New balance			
Birthdays/Christmas			
Car insurance			
Car MOT/service/tax			
Childcare			
Clothing/shoes			
Council tax			
Dentist/optician			
Electricity			
Entertainment			
Gas/oil/solid fuel			
Groceries			
Hairdresser			
Holidays			
Home/pet insurance			
Life/medical insurance			
Mobile/phone/internet			
Mortgage/rent			
Newspapers/magazines			
Petrol/fares			
Pets			
Savings			
Subscriptions			
TV licence/satellite			
Water			
Total expenditure			
Closing balance			

HOME BUDGETING

	JULY	AUGUST	SEPTEMBER
Opening balance			
Income			
New balance			
Birthdays/Christmas			
Car insurance			
Car MOT/service/tax			
Childcare			
Clothing/shoes			
Council tax			
Dentist/optician			
Electricity			
Entertainment			
Gas/oil/solid fuel			
Groceries			
Hairdresser			
Holidays			
Home/pet insurance			
Life/medical insurance			
Mobile/phone/internet			
Mortgage/rent			
Newspapers/magazines			
Petrol/fares			
Pets			
Savings			
Subscriptions			
TV licence/satellite			
Water			
Total expenditure			
Closing balance			

	OCTOBER	NOVEMBER	DECEMBER
Opening balance			
Income			
New balance			
Birthdays/Christmas			
Car insurance			
Car MOT/service/tax			
Childcare			
Clothing/shoes			
Council tax			
Dentist/optician			
Electricity			
Entertainment			
Gas/oil/solid fuel			
Groceries			
Hairdresser			
Holidays			
Home/pet insurance			
Life/medical insurance			
Mobile/phone/internet			
Mortgage/rent			
Newspapers/magazines			
Petrol/fares			
Pets			
Savings			
Subscriptions			
TV licence/satellite			
Water			
Total expenditure			
Closing balance			

2021

January
Mon		4	11	18	25
Tue		5	12	19	26
Wed		6	13	20	27
Thu		7	14	21	28
Fri	1	8	15	22	29
Sat	2	9	16	23	30
Sun	3	10	17	24	31

February
Mon	1	8	15	22
Tue	2	9	16	23
Wed	3	10	17	24
Thu	4	11	18	25
Fri	5	12	19	26
Sat	6	13	20	27
Sun	7	14	21	28

March
Mon	1	8	15	22	29
Tue	2	9	16	23	30
Wed	3	10	17	24	31
Thu	4	11	18	25
Fri	5	12	19	26
Sat	6	13	20	27
Sun	7	14	21	28

April
Mon		5	12	19	26
Tue		6	13	20	27
Wed		7	14	21	28
Thu	1	8	15	22	29
Fri	2	9	16	23	30
Sat	3	10	17	24
Sun	4	11	18	25

May
Mon		3	10	17	24	31
Tue		4	11	18	25
Wed		5	12	19	26
Thu		6	13	20	27
Fri		7	14	21	28
Sat	1	8	15	22	29
Sun	2	9	16	23	30

June
Mon		7	14	21	28
Tue	1	8	15	22	29
Wed	2	9	16	23	30
Thu	3	10	17	24
Fri	4	11	18	25
Sat	5	12	19	26
Sun	6	13	20	27

July
Mon		5	12	19	26
Tue		6	13	20	27
Wed		7	14	21	28
Thu	1	8	15	22	29
Fri	2	9	16	23	30
Sat	3	10	17	24	31
Sun	4	11	18	25

August
Mon	2	9	16	23	30
Tue	3	10	17	24	31
Wed	4	11	18	25
Thu	5	12	19	26
Fri	6	13	20	27
Sat	7	14	21	28
Sun	1	8	15	22	29

September
Mon		6	13	20	27
Tue		7	14	21	28
Wed	1	8	15	22	29
Thu	2	9	16	23	30
Fri	3	10	17	24
Sat	4	11	18	25
Sun	5	12	19	26

October
Mon		4	11	18	25
Tue		5	12	19	26
Wed		6	13	20	27
Thu		7	14	21	28
Fri	1	8	15	22	29
Sat	2	9	16	23	30
Sun	3	10	17	24	31

November
Mon	1	8	15	22	29
Tue	2	9	16	23	30
Wed	3	10	17	24
Thu	4	11	18	25
Fri	5	12	19	26
Sat	6	13	20	27
Sun	7	14	21	28

December
Mon		6	13	20	27
Tue		7	14	21	28
Wed	1	8	15	22	29
Thu	2	9	16	23	30
Fri	3	10	17	24	31
Sat	4	11	18	25
Sun	5	12	19	26

2023

January
Mon	2	9	16	23	30
Tue	3	10	17	24	31
Wed	4	11	18	25
Thu	5	12	19	26
Fri	6	13	20	27
Sat	7	14	21	28
Sun	1	8	15	22	29

February
Mon		6	13	20	27
Tue		7	14	21	28
Wed	1	8	15	22
Thu	2	9	16	23
Fri	3	10	17	24
Sat	4	11	18	25
Sun	5	12	19	26

March
Mon		6	13	20	27
Tue		7	14	21	28
Wed	1	8	15	22	29
Thu	2	9	16	23	30
Fri	3	10	17	24	31
Sat	4	11	18	25
Sun	5	12	19	26

April
Mon		3	10	17	24
Tue		4	11	18	25
Wed		5	12	19	26
Thu		6	13	20	27
Fri		7	14	21	28
Sat	1	8	15	22	29
Sun	2	9	16	23	30

May
Mon	1	8	15	22	29
Tue	2	9	16	23	30
Wed	3	10	17	24	31
Thu	4	11	18	25
Fri	5	12	19	26
Sat	6	13	20	27
Sun	7	14	21	28

June
Mon		5	12	19	26
Tue		6	13	20	27
Wed		7	14	21	28
Thu	1	8	15	22	29
Fri	2	9	16	23	30
Sat	3	10	17	24
Sun	4	11	18	25

July
Mon		3	10	17	24	31
Tue		4	11	18	25
Wed		5	12	19	26
Thu		6	13	20	27
Fri		7	14	21	28
Sat	1	8	15	22	29
Sun	2	9	16	23	30

August
Mon		7	14	21	28
Tue	1	8	15	22	29
Wed	2	9	16	23	30
Thu	3	10	17	24	31
Fri	4	11	18	25
Sat	5	12	19	26
Sun	6	13	20	27

September
Mon		4	11	18	25
Tue		5	12	19	26
Wed		6	13	20	27
Thu		7	14	21	28
Fri	1	8	15	22	29
Sat	2	9	16	23	30
Sun	3	10	17	24

October
Mon	2	9	16	23	30
Tue	3	10	17	24	31
Wed	4	11	18	25
Thu	5	12	19	26
Fri	6	13	20	27
Sat	7	14	21	28
Sun	1	8	15	22	29

November
Mon		6	13	20	27
Tue		7	14	21	28
Wed	1	8	15	22	29
Thu	2	9	16	23	30
Fri	3	10	17	24
Sat	4	11	18	25
Sun	5	12	19	26

December
Mon		4	11	18	25
Tue		5	12	19	26
Wed		6	13	20	27
Thu		7	14	21	28
Fri	1	8	15	22	29
Sat	2	9	16	23	30
Sun	3	10	17	24	31

2022

JANUARY

Mon		3	10	17	24	31
Tue		4	11	18	25	
Wed		5	12	19	26	
Thu		6	13	20	27	
Fri		7	14	21	28	
Sat	1	8	15	22	29	
Sun	2	9	16	23	30	

FEBRUARY

Mon		7	14	21	28
Tue	1	8	15	22	
Wed	2	9	16	23	
Thu	3	10	17	24	
Fri	4	11	18	25	
Sat	5	12	19	26	
Sun	6	13	20	27	

MARCH

Mon		7	14	21	28
Tue	1	8	15	22	29
Wed	2	9	16	23	30
Thu	3	10	17	24	31
Fri	4	11	18	25	
Sat	5	12	19	26	
Sun	6	13	20	27	

APRIL

Mon		4	11	18	25
Tue		5	12	19	26
Wed		6	13	20	27
Thu		7	14	21	28
Fri	1	8	15	22	29
Sat	2	9	16	23	30
Sun	3	10	17	24	

MAY

Mon		2	9	16	23	30
Tue		3	10	17	24	31
Wed		4	11	18	25	
Thu		5	12	19	26	
Fri		6	13	20	27	
Sat		7	14	21	28	
Sun	1	8	15	22	29	

JUNE

Mon		6	13	20	27
Tue		7	14	21	28
Wed	1	8	15	22	29
Thu	2	9	16	23	30
Fri	3	10	17	24	
Sat	4	11	18	25	
Sun	5	12	19	26	

JULY

Mon		4	11	18	25
Tue		5	12	19	26
Wed		6	13	20	27
Thu		7	14	21	28
Fri	1	8	15	22	29
Sat	2	9	16	23	30
Sun	3	10	17	24	31

AUGUST

Mon	1	8	15	22	29
Tue	2	9	16	23	30
Wed	3	10	17	24	31
Thu	4	11	18	25	
Fri	5	12	19	26	
Sat	6	13	20	27	
Sun	7	14	21	28	

SEPTEMBER

Mon		5	12	19	26
Tue		6	13	20	27
Wed		7	14	21	28
Thu	1	8	15	22	29
Fri	2	9	16	23	30
Sat	3	10	17	24	
Sun	4	11	18	25	

OCTOBER

Mon		3	10	17	24	31
Tue		4	11	18	25	
Wed		5	12	19	26	
Thu		6	13	20	27	
Fri		7	14	21	28	
Sat	1	8	15	22	29	
Sun	2	9	16	23	30	

NOVEMBER

Mon		7	14	21	28
Tue	1	8	15	22	29
Wed	2	9	16	23	30
Thu	3	10	17	24	
Fri	4	11	18	25	
Sat	5	12	19	26	
Sun	6	13	20	27	

DECEMBER

Mon		5	12	19	26
Tue		6	13	20	27
Wed		7	14	21	28
Thu	1	8	15	22	29
Fri	2	9	16	23	30
Sat	3	10	17	24	31
Sun	4	11	18	25	

Calendar dates

UK HOLIDAYS †	2022	2023
New Year	Jan 3*	Jan 2*
New Year (Scotland)	Jan 3/4*	Jan 2/3*
St Patrick's Day (Northern Ireland)	Mar 17	Mar 17
Good Friday	Apr 15	Apr 7
Easter Monday	Apr 18	Apr 10
Early Spring	May 2	May 1
Spring	–	May 29
Elizabeth II's 70th Anniversary celebrations	Jun 2/3	–
Battle of the Boyne (Northern Ireland)	Jul 12	Jul 12
Summer (Scotland)	Aug 1	Aug 7
Summer (except Scotland)	Aug 29	Aug 28
Christmas Day	Dec 27*	Dec 25
Boxing Day	Dec 26	Dec 26

NOTABLE DATES	2022
Burns' Night	Jan 25
Holocaust Memorial Day	Jan 27
Accession of Queen Elizabeth II	Feb 6
Chinese New Year – Year of the Tiger	Feb 1
St Valentine's Day	Feb 14
Shrove Tuesday (Pancake Day)	Mar 1
St David's Day (Wales)	Mar 1
Commonwealth Day	Mar 14
St Patrick's Day (Ireland)	Mar 17
Mothering Sunday	Mar 27
Birthday of Queen Elizabeth II	Apr 21
St George's Day (England)	Apr 23
World Red Cross/Red Crescent Day	May 8
Coronation Day	Jun 2
Queen's Official Birthday (t.b.c.)	Jun 11
Father's Day	Jun 19
Armed Forces' Day	Jun 25
St Swithin's Day	Jul 15
International Day of Peace	Sep 21
United Nations Day	Oct 24
Halloween	Oct 31
Armistice Day	Nov 11
Remembrance Sunday	Nov 13
Birthday of the Prince of Wales	Nov 14
St Andrew's Day (Scotland)	Nov 30

RELIGIOUS DATES

Christian

Epiphany	Jan 6
Ash Wednesday	Mar 2
Palm Sunday	Apr 10
Good Friday	Apr 15
Easter Day	Apr 17
Ascension Day, Holy Thursday	May 26
Whit Sunday, Pentecost	Jun 5
Trinity Sunday	Jun 12
Corpus Christi	Jun 16
Advent Sunday	Nov 27
Christmas Day	Dec 25

Buddhist

Parinirvana Day	Feb 15
Wesak (Buddha Day)	May 8
Bodhi Day (Buddha's enlightenment)	Dec 8

Hindu

Maha Shivaratri	Feb 28
Holi	Mar 18
Navaratri begins	Sep 26
Diwali begins (also celebrated by Sikhs)	Oct 24

Islamic

Ramadan begins	Apr 3
Eid Ul-Fitr	May 3
Eid Ul-Adha	Jul 10
Al-Hijra (New Year)	Jul 30
Milad un Nabi (Prophet's birthday)	Oct 8

Jewish

Purim begins	Mar 17
Pesach (Passover) begins	Apr 16
Shavuot (Pentecost) begins	Jun 5
Rosh Hashanah (Jewish New Year)	Sep 26
Yom Kippur (Day of Atonement)	Oct 5
Succoth (Tabernacles) begins	Oct 10
Chanukah begins	Dec 19

Sikh

These dates follow the Nanakshahi calendar

Birthday of Guru Gobind Singh	Jan 5
Vaisakhi	Apr 14
Birthday of Guru Nanak	Apr 14
Martyrdom of Guru Arjan Dev	Jun 16
Martyrdom of Guru Tegh Bahadur	Nov 24

Note: Many religious dates are based on the lunar calendar and, therefore, we cannot guarantee their accuracy.

†Bank Holiday dates can change
*Substitute Bank Holidays (when the date falls on a Saturday or Sunday)

PHASES OF THE MOON

● New moon			) First quarter		
	Day	H:M		Day	H:M
Jan	2	18:33	Jan	9	18:11
Feb	1	05:46	Feb	8	13:50
Mar	2	17:35	Mar	10	10:45
Apr	1	06:24	Apr	9	06:48
Apr	30	20:28	May	9	00:21
May	30	11:30	Jun	7	14:49
Jun	29	02:52	Jul	7	02:14
Jul	28	17:55	Aug	5	11:07
Aug	27	08:17	Sep	3	18:08
Sep	25	21:55	Oct	3	00:14
Oct	25	10:49	Nov	1	06:37
Nov	23	22:57	Nov	30	14:37
Dec	23	10:17	Dec	30	01:21

○ Full moon			(Last quarter		
	Day	H:M		Day	H:M
Jan	17	23:48	Jan	25	13:41
Feb	16	16:57	Feb	23	22:32
Mar	18	07:18	Mar	25	05:37
Apr	16	18:55	Apr	23	11:56
May	16	04:14	May	22	18:43
Jun	14	11:52	Jun	21	03:11
Jul	13	18:38	Jul	20	14:19
Aug	12	01:36	Aug	19	04:36
Sep	10	09:59	Sep	17	21:52
Oct	9	20:55	Oct	17	17:15
Nov	8	11.02	Nov	16	13:27
Dec	8	04:08	Dec	16	08:56

BRITISH SUMMERTIME (t.b.c. by Government)

▶ Clocks go forward 1 hour at 1am on 27 March

◀ Clocks go back 1 hour at 2am on 30 October

SEASONS

	Month	Day	H:M
Vernal equinox Spring begins	Mar	20	15:33
Summer solstice Summer begins	June	21	09:14
Autumnal equinox Autumn begins	Sep	23	01:04
Winter solstice Winter begins	Dec	21	21:48

WEBSITES

gov.uk/bank-holidays

when-is.com

SUNRISE AND SUNSET TIMES

Note: times vary – these are for London

Day	Rise H:M	Set H:M	Day	Rise H:M	Set H:M	Day	Rise H:M	Set H:M	Day	Rise H:M	Set H:M
January			**February**			**March**			**April**		
07	08:05	16:09	07	07:29	17:01	07	06:33	17:51	07	06:23	19:44
14	08:00	16:19	14	07:17	17:14	14	06:17	18:03	14	06:07	19:56
21	07:54	16:31	21	07:03	17:26	21	06:01	18:15	21	05:53	20:07
28	07:45	16:43	28	06:48	17:39	28	06:45	19:27	28	05:39	20:19
May			**June**			**July**			**August**		
07	05:22	20:34	07	04:45	21:14	07	04:53	21:18	07	05:33	20:38
14	05:11	20:44	14	04:43	21:19	14	05:00	21:13	14	05:44	20:25
21	05:01	20:55	21	04:43	21:22	21	05:09	21:05	21	05:56	20:11
28	04:53	21:04	28	04:46	21:22	28	05:18	20:55	28	06:07	19:56
September			**October**			**November**			**December**		
07	06:23	19:34	07	07:11	18:25	07	07:05	16:23	07	07:52	15:52
14	06:34	19:18	14	07:23	18:10	14	07:17	16:13	14	07:59	15:52
21	06:45	19:02	21	07:35	17:55	21	07:29	16:04	21	08:04	15:54
28	06:56	18:45	28	07:47	17:41	28	07:39	15:57	28	08:06	15:58

Anniversaries

LAST MAN ON THE MOON
50 years

Only twenty-four astronauts have been to the moon, and just twelve of these actually set foot on the lunar surface.

The last to do so was Apollo 17 commander Eugene Cernan on 14 December 1972. Apollo 11, led by Neil Armstrong, is the most well-known of the moon missions, when man first walked on the moon in 1969. It was a huge moment in human and scientific history. So why did we stop going to the moon just three years later?

President John F. Kennedy had made it his mission to land an American on the moon. This goal makes sense against the backdrop of the Cold War Space Race, which was kickstarted by Russia's successful launch of Sputnik (the first artificial Earth satellite) in 1957. There was real panic that the USA was falling behind in this proxy war, hence Kennedy's push to catch up.

After the success of Apollo 11, Americans felt that they'd well and truly won the race. Travelling to the moon was eye-wateringly expensive (the moonwalk cost around $288 billion in today's money) and President Nixon enacted huge cuts to NASA's budget. Plans for the final three Apollo missions were shelved in 1970.

The fact that humankind has never returned to the moon has added fuel to the fire of conspiracy theories that claim men never walked on the moon in the first place. NASA's Artemis Program plans to return humans to the moon in the 2020s. Perhaps that will set any doubters to rest!

2022 ANNIVERSARIES

500: Spanish seafarer Juan Sebastián de Elcano completes the first circumnavigation of the globe (8 September 1522)

400: The Papal Chancery adopts 1 January as the first day of the year in place of 25 March (1622)

200: The Royal Academy of Music is established in London (date unknown, 1822)

175: Charlotte Brontë publishes *Jane Eyre* under the pen name Currer Bell (16 October 1847)

150: Yellowstone in the western US becomes the world's first national park (1 March 1872)

150: The Metropolitan Museum of Art, known informally as the Met, opens in New York City (20 February 1872)

100: The first successful treatment of diabetes with insulin is performed in Toronto, Canada (11 January 1922)

100: The British Broadcasting Corporation (BBC) is formed (18 October 1922)

100: British archaeologist Howard Carter finds the entrance to Egyptian Pharaoh Tutankhamun's tomb in the Valley of the Kings of Egypt (4 November 1922)

75: Princess Elizabeth (later Elizabeth II) marries The Duke of Edinburgh at Westminster Abbey (20 November 1947)

70: Queen Elizabeth II declared Queen of the United Kingdom of Great Britain and Northern Ireland after the death of George VI (6 February 1952)

40: The first Dairy Diary is released, selling over 1½ million copies in its first year (1982)

40: Michael Jackson releases *Thriller*, which would become one of the bestselling albums ever (30 November 1982)

25: The Labour Party returns to power for the first time in 18 years, with Tony Blair as Prime Minister, in a landslide majority (2 May 1997)

25: Diana, Princess of Wales dies in a car accident in the Pont de l'Alma road tunnel in Paris (31 August 1997)

20: The Queen Mother dies in her sleep at the age of 101 in Windsor (30 March 2002)

10: The Summer Olympic Games are held in London (27 July–12 August 2012)

BRING OUT THE BRANSTON

100 years

For many Brits, a picnic simply isn't a picnic without a jar of Branston pickle. For others, a bite of a cheese and pickle sandwich takes them right back to their school days.

The quintessential British condiment is celebrating 100 years in production since its creation by food company Crosse & Blackwell in the Staffordshire village of Branston. The pickle is still made using the original recipe. The exact quantities are a closely held secret, but it includes a mixture of diced carrots, onion and swede pickled in a sauce made with vinegar, tomatoes and apples. Some 17 million jars fly off UK shelves every year!

THE FIRST EDITION OF *DRACULA*

125 years

Very few names send shivers down the spine like that of Dracula. The notorious vampire was first brought to life by author Bram Stoker in his 1897 Gothic horror novel of the same name.

The inaugural edition of the book was published by Archibald Constable and Company, London, in May 1897, and sold for 6 shillings. The title *Dracula* was actually an eleventh-hour alteration; the novel's title had been *The Un-Dead* until just weeks before publication.

The plot follows Count Dracula, a 15th century prince, who is condemned to live off the blood of the living for eternity, as he attempts to move from Transylvania to England to spread the un-dead curse.

While *Dracula* was not an instant bestseller upon publication, the sheer number of reworkings and adaptations it has inspired is the real marker of its extraordinary success. Count Dracula remains one of literature's most immediately recognisable characters to this day, and Stoker's story launched the vampire trope that has since been seen in countless horror films and books as well as many direct adaptations of Stoker's novel.

ANNIVERSARY & BIRTHDAY GIFT RECORD

WEDDINGS

1	Paper	14	Ivory
2	Cotton	15	Crystal
3	Leather	20	China
4	Books	25	Silver
5	Wood	30	Pearl
6	Iron	35	Coral
7	Wool	40	Ruby
8	Bronze	45	Sapphire
9	Copper	50	Gold
10	Tin	55	Emerald
11	Steel	60	Diamond
12	Silk	65	Blue
	or linen		Sapphire
13	Lace	70	Platinum

BIRTHSTONES AND FLOWERS

Month	Birthstone	Flower
January	Garnet	Carnation
February	Amethyst	Violet
March	Aquamarine	Jonquil
April	Diamond	Sweet Pea
May	Emerald	Lily of the Valley
June	Pearl	Rose
July	Ruby	Larkspur
August	Peridot	Gladiolus
September	Sapphire	Aster
October	Opal	Calendula
November	Topaz	Chrysanthemum
December	Turquoise	Narcissus

Name	Date	Ideas	Bought	Cost

ANNIVERSARY & BIRTHDAY GIFT RECORD

Name	Date	Ideas	Bought	Cost

A 'Could Do' list for 2022

Feel too busy to plan anything for pleasure? Tied to your to-do list? Enter the 'Could Do' list. Using this guilt-free method, you can put fun at the forefront and make time for the things you truly enjoy.

Do you have a to-do list? You might even have more than one: a list of chores, a tally of work tasks, perhaps a note of birthday cards you need to write, and a shopping list almost certainly. But have you got a 'Could Do' list?

This isn't a list of optional errands, or tasks you think you *should* do. Rather, it's a personalised list of enjoyable, nourishing or novel activities – things you've always wanted to try, but have never made a proper priority.

TAKE OFF THE PRESSURE

In a nutshell, a 'Could Do' list is similar to a bucket list, defined as a number of experiences or achievements that a person hopes to have or accomplish in their lifetime, but it comes without the pressure or expense that bucket lists traditionally imply.

While an aspirational bucket list is certainly good fun to put together, dreams like 'take a round-the-world trip', 'climb Mount Kilimanjaro' or 'swim with dolphins' require a significant amount of time and money, which can both feel out of reach for many.

A 'Could Do' list is a bit like an achievable bucket list, filled with ideas for things to do that you could take up with little notice. It shouldn't leave you feeling filled with regret if you haven't been able to achieve everything, or even most of the things, on the list.

BRAINSTORM IDEAS

Set aside a little time to dream up ideas for your own 'Could Do' list. Start small – remember this isn't necessarily about big-ticket goals or once-in-a-lifetime ambitions. Instead, think about everyday activities you like doing but never seem to find time for.

Ponder new hobbies or skills you'd like to take up or learn. Think about events or sites of interest near your home that you've been meaning to visit for years. Is there a dish you've always wanted to learn how to make? Or a sport you've always planned to have a go at playing with friends?

The key detail when creating a 'Could Do' list is that anything goes, and nothing is too small or trivial to make the cut!

GUILT-FREE GOALS

The best thing about a 'Could Do' list is that it can be totally guilt-free. Because the items on the list are merely suggestions, a range of ideas to inspire you, it does not announce itself with all the weighty pressures of your average list. Ideally, it will be filled with attainable goals.

A 'Could Do' list is all about pleasure, about the things that interest and intrigue you, about the activities that feed your soul. It is about releasing the pressure of the 'shoulds' and the 'have-tos'.

IT'S UP TO YOU

Experiment, if you like, with different ways of structuring your list. Maybe you'd like to structure it around the seasons, or write a list for the whole year. You could lay out your list by activity, separating cooking could-dos from trips you'd like to take. Leave room to add to your ideas at the bottom, for when inspiration strikes.

'Could Do' list suggestions

- [ ] Have a go at indoor or outdoor mini golf
- [ ] Hire a rowing boat or a pedalo
- [ ] Attend a cocktail mixology class
- [ ] Go on a British safari
- [ ] Host a supper club with friends or family
- [ ] Visit a local food and drink festival
- [ ] Take part in a colour run or charity walk
- [ ] Pick a partner and try ballroom dancing
- [ ] Write a letter thanking a person who has been a positive influence in your life
- [ ] Discover a 'secret' cocktail bar
- [ ] Make an insect hotel in your garden
- [ ] Visit a bee farm and taste local honey
- [ ] Take a floral artistry class
- [ ] Scale a climbing wall
- [ ] Have fun at a roller disco
- [ ] Take your friends or family ice-skating
- [ ] Make a sand sculpture at the seaside
- [ ] Enjoy a pottery painting day
- [ ] Host your own afternoon tea
- [ ] Create your own time capsule to look back on in 10 years
- [ ] Volunteer in your community
- [ ] Visit National Trust properties or events
- [ ] Go to an open-air concert or outdoor cinema
- [ ] Eat out at a museum or art gallery café (and view some exhibits while you're there!)
- [ ] Ride on a steam train
- [ ] Climb a hill and capture the view in each season
- [ ] Visit a castle or palace
- [ ] Picnic by a river (and take a dip if you fancy!)
- [ ] Read a book under a tree
- [ ] Learn to count to 20 in a foreign language (try duolingo.com)
- [ ] Teach yourself how to use chopsticks
- [ ] Go to the theatre to see a play you've never seen before
- [ ] Learn how to practise mindfulness
- [ ] Paint a portrait of a family member or pet
- [ ] Go to a live stand-up comedy show
- [ ] Learn a few yoga poses (see our tips on p30)
- [ ] Bake your own bread
- [ ] Cook a recipe you've never tried before
- [ ] Watch a sunrise and sunset on the same day
- [ ] Research your family tree
- [ ] Sew a patchwork 'memory quilt' with scraps of fabrics from meaningful garments or items
- [ ] Try making an origami crane
- [ ] Ask someone to tell you a story about their life that you've not heard before
- [ ] Donate to a charity whose work inspires you
- [ ] Get lost on purpose
- [ ] Read a classic novel
- [ ] Attend a wine or cheese tasting (or a wine *and* cheese tasting!)

Your 'Could Do' list

- [ ] _____
- [ ] _____
- [ ] _____
- [ ] _____
- [ ] _____
- [ ] _____
- [ ] _____
- [ ] _____
- [ ] _____
- [ ] _____
- [ ] _____
- [ ] _____
- [ ] _____
- [ ] _____
- [ ] _____
- [ ] _____
- [ ] _____
- [ ] _____
- [ ] _____
- [ ] _____
- [ ] _____
- [ ] _____
- [ ] _____
- [ ] _____
- [ ] _____
- [ ] _____

- [ ] _____
- [ ] _____
- [ ] _____
- [ ] _____
- [ ] _____
- [ ] _____
- [ ] _____
- [ ] _____
- [ ] _____
- [ ] _____
- [ ] _____
- [ ] _____
- [ ] _____
- [ ] _____
- [ ] _____
- [ ] _____
- [ ] _____
- [ ] _____
- [ ] _____
- [ ] _____
- [ ] _____
- [ ] _____
- [ ] _____
- [ ] _____
- [ ] _____
- [ ] _____

Say yes to yoga

Fancy being more flexible, improving your concentration and achieving better posture? These are just some of the benefits of a regular yoga practice. And despite its booming trendiness, there's a style and pace of this ancient form of exercise for everyone – whatever your age, fitness level or agility.

Yoga is a form of physical and mental exercise that originated in India 5,000 years ago, although the precise details of its genesis remain unknown. The word yoga comes from the Sanskrit for 'union', emphasising yoga's focus on connecting the body and higher self.

If you are new to yoga, start by attending a class. This way, you can safely learn the basics from a qualified teacher, who will be able to check your postural alignment and advise on adjustments. As yoga is now popular across the UK, it shouldn't be too difficult to find a class at your local leisure centre or village hall. Classes last 45-90 minutes and styles of yoga vary widely, from energetic vinyasa flow to calmer hatha yoga. Pick a type that suits your age and agility.

The foundations of yoga are the poses – a series of standing or sitting movements that increase strength and flexibility. Many poses aim to improve balance by strengthening the lower limbs, in particular the knees and ankles. This can reduce the risk of falls and osteoporosis.

Yoga's second focus is the breath, also a powerful way to connect to your body. Yoga breath requires you to inhale and exhale through the nose, allowing your breathing to deepen and slow. This helps to open up the body, centre one's attention and encourage a focus on the current moment.

Practising yoga comes with a host of benefits for body and mind.

Practising yoga comes with a host of physical benefits. It can help to manage high blood pressure and back pain, improve balance and promote better sleep. There is evidence that it can even ease mild depression, and many use yoga to alleviate stress. It's also a fabulous way to improve concentration – there are no distractions on the mat. It's just you, your body and your breath.

3 YOGA POSES FOR BEGINNERS

Child's Pose (Balasana)
This is a calming pose that is used for restful pauses between more difficult postures. It helps to elongate the muscles of the lower back.
How to: On the floor, lower your hips to your heels and rest your forehead on the floor. Your knees can be together or apart. Lay your arms overhead with your knees on the floor.

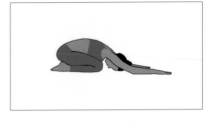

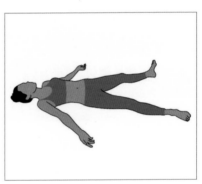

Downward-Facing Dog (Adho Mukha Svanasana)
One of the most well-known yoga poses, this posture offers a revitalising, full-body stretch.
How to: Start by kneeling on your hands and knees on the mat, in the shape of a table. Spread out your palms and place your knees and feet hip-distance apart, curling your toes. Walk your palms forward until just over your shoulders, then raise your knees off the mat and lift your hips up high into the air until your legs are straight. Bend your knees, if needed, and keep your toes pointing forward. You should look like an upside down 'V' shape.

Corpse Pose (Savasana)
This is a pose for total relaxation. Most types of yoga begin and end with this grounding posture.
How to: Lie with your back on the floor with your arms stretched out by your sides and your legs flat on the mat, feet pointing up. Gradually relax one body part at a time, starting from the toes, letting go of any thoughts that arise as you do so. Maintain this pose for five minutes for maximum effect. When you're ready to get up, don't stand up straight away: instead, roll onto one side and push yourself up with your hands to avoid dizziness.

TRY A CLASS FOR FREE

The NHS Fitness Studio, available on the NHS website, offers several yoga class videos that you can try from the comfort of your own home. Most are suitable for beginners (though it's worth checking the class description). All you need to get started is a yoga mat. If you don't have a mat, you can use a clean towel or blanket laid out on the floor.

If you're keen to try yoga to deal with a specific issue, take a look at 'Yoga with Adriene' on YouTube, where there are hundreds of videos available to try at home for free. You can search by body part or ailment ('yoga for back pain', for example, or 'yoga for stress'), or jump right in with the first video you find! It helps to practise near a mirror so you can check your posture.

WEBSITES
nhs.uk/conditions/nhs-fitness-studio
yogaclassnearyou.co.uk   iyengaryoga.org.uk
yogaindailylife.org.uk   yogawithadriene.com
bwy.org.uk   traditionalyoga.co.uk

Why helping others is healthy

'Do unto others as you would have them do unto you' is a phrase we're all familiar with, but did you know helping others can help us to feel good about ourselves, too?

Cast your mind back to the last time you did something nice for somebody else. Perhaps you dished up an extra helping of lasagne for the new parents next door, or allowed a fellow shopper to jump ahead of you in the supermarket queue. Do you remember how it felt when you saw their surprise, followed by a smile on their face? There's that little hum of happiness, the feel-good sensation of altruism and often the big smile that emerges on your own face in turn. It made you feel pretty good, didn't it?

Supporting others can reduce our own stress levels.

This 'feeling' is not merely hearsay. There's actually a scientific explanation for the buoyant sensation that arises when we help another person out. To begin understanding this, we must travel back to the time of our ancient ancestors. We are hardwired for connection and offering someone assistance in the days when humans lived on the savanna may have aided one's own survival. If you offered a helping hand to someone in need, the hope was that maybe they'd help you out when you needed it most in the future.

VOLUNTEER BENEFITS

While assisting a friend might not confer the same survival benefits as it did in the distant past, studies show that helping others could contribute to a longer lifespan in other ways. Supporting others can reduce our own stress levels (leading to lower risk of disease) and decrease loneliness, which can affect both physical and mental health.

Becoming a volunteer is an admirable way to commit to helping others. Is there a cause you're particularly passionate about, or a local charity or organisation you're well-placed to support? Helping others on a regular basis – whether it's assisting pupils with reading or a weekly call with an isolated elderly person – also connects you to others. As well as being a boon to those you're helping, it will increase your self-confidence in the process. By measuring brain activity in volunteers, researchers have even discovered that supporting others gives us great pleasure on a chemical level. Ergo, the more we give, the happier we feel.

INCREASE WELLBEING

If a regular volunteering commitment is beyond you right now, try a small gesture. Smiling at a stranger, checking on a neighbour or leaving seeds out for the birds confers the same feel-good benefits.

The rewards are multitude. Scientific studies reveal that helping others out can make our lives more meaningful, increase our sense of satisfaction, and potentially even lower blood pressure. A 2019 Finnish study found that exercising compassion boosts our moods and makes us more contented.

The best thing is that, mostly, when we help others out, we're not doing it to enrich ourselves. The extra benefits are an unexpected side effect, albeit a fantastic one. Help others because you care and reap rewards that enrich your own sense of self in the process? It's a win-win situation. So what are you waiting for?

12 SIMPLE WAYS TO HELP YOUR FRIENDS, FAMILY AND COMMUNITY

1 Take the time to write a heartfelt thank you note after receiving a gift.

2 Offer to help an elderly neighbour or relative with tasks they find difficult, perhaps doing the food shop, or mowing their lawn.

3 Give a genuine smile to those you encounter while out and about.

4 For a friend or relative's birthday, write a list of happy memories you have shared together and turn it into a scrapbook complete with printed photos and mementos.

5 Sign up to give blood, if you are able to.

6 Pass on a book you really loved to someone you think would enjoy it.

7 If you have a special interest or skill – maybe you're a star gardener, or can speak another language – offer to teach it to someone in your life who has previously expressed an interest in learning it. Or you could teach a child in your life how to ride a bike, or instruct a technophobe on how to send an email.

8 Enjoyed a delicious meal at your local pub, or really enjoyed visiting a small museum on your holidays? Take time to leave a glowing review so that others will be able to enjoy it as well.

9 Ever find yourself thinking how grateful you are for your partner, what a great job your colleague has done, or how well that colour of jumper suits your friend? Tell them so!

10 Donate unworn clothes or blankets to a homeless shelter or women's refuge.

11 Organise or join in with a community litter-picking session in your local area.

12 Look out for small acts of kindness you can offer throughout the day: hold the door or pay for the coffee of the person behind you.

Make do & mend

Fixing is back in fashion! Growing scrutiny of single-use culture means that our relationship with what we own is in flux. In the face of environmental concerns, the wartime concept of 'Make Do and Mend' is enjoying a renewed lease of life across the country.

The phrase 'Make Do and Mend' was coined during the Second World War, when the government introduced a campaign of the same name. The aim of the scheme was to motivate the country to reuse and repair their existing clothes so that fabric production could be pivoted to produce military uniforms and other wartime essentials. Advice in the accompanying leaflets also included tips on how to make clothing coupons go further: in Britain, rationing of clothes, fabric and wool began in 1941 and would last until 1949. Tutorials taught thrifty citizens how to prevent moth damage to clothing, darn holes in socks and make clothes for children from adult garments. As a result, handmade and revitalised clothes were commonplace in 1940s Britain: men's suits were turned into skirts and jackets for women, jumpers were unravelled to obtain spare wool for darning socks, and garment exchanges helped parents clothe their growing children.

BACK IN VOGUE

Today, more than 80 years on, repair culture is back in vogue, and the phrase 'make do and mend' endures in a broader sense, relating to the repair of the possessions one already owns – instead of throwing out something broken and buying a replacement.

Having experienced renewed popularity following the 2008 recession, the make do and mend spirit has continued to gain prominence as worries about the environment – and the human impact on it – have grown. Though its original meaning related to clothing, the expression now applies to any and all consumer goods.

WHY REPAIR?

There have been increasing distress calls from politicians and the general public about the throwaway culture of consumerism. When it's much cheaper to buy a new kettle when your old one sputters out its last cuppa, why bother looking into a repair?

Many technology companies charge so much to mend their own goods that it's often a false economy to do so. There's also the alarming fact that between 2004 and 2012, the amount of household appliances that kicked the bucket within five years of being bought doubled.

Western societies have become trapped in a cycle of buying cheap goods, which inevitably break, then having little choice but to throw these out and purchase replacements. While this may have worked for a while, with resources running out and increased awareness of the climate crisis, there's never been a better time to make the most of what you've got.

Thankfully we don't have to go it alone when it comes to making and mending. A burgeoning national collective of so-called repair cafés have sprung up in the hopes of giving a new lease of life to worn or broken household items.

The first repair café was dreamt up by Dutch environmentalist Martine Postma in 2009 after she found herself increasingly frustrated with throwaway culture. Broken hair dryers, rusting secateurs, rickety sewing machines and holey tea towels are just some of the things that you might see fixed at your average repair event. The cafés tend to be run by volunteers and foster a sense of community and togetherness.

GENUINE JOY

There's a real feel-good thrill that comes from learning to mend your own possessions, not to mention a reduction in the guilt that comes from throwing broken items away. At repair cafés, the item in question is always repaired with the owner present, helping to demystify the process of fixing.

The aim is for the owner to learn how to mend their possessions themselves in future by watching the repair process in action. It's not just a circular economy, but a circular learning process, as many repair café volunteers were once customers on the other side of the table.

LIBRARY OF THINGS

The make do and mend ethos also means buying less in the first place. So-called libraries of things have sprung up to address this need, loaning out household items as regular libraries do books. Several exist around the country, including in London, Frome and Edinburgh, with more set to open.

The goal is to make borrowing more attractive than buying and to increase access to occasional-use devices, whether it's a sander for smoothing your floorboards or a pressure washer that most people would only find use for once a year.

For these kinds of objects, borrowing – saving money and reducing consumption in the process – makes a lot of sense. Especially when you learn that, on average, a drill is used for just 13 minutes of its lifetime. Some libraries of things charge a nominal fee or suggest a donation, while others are free at the point of use. Similar initiatives exist for more specific items: sling libraries, where parents can try out different baby carriers, are becoming common, and toy swap shops are also gaining in popularity.

EXCHANGING SKILLS

Creating a society that values mending and reusing items has many benefits. Some of these are immediately obvious: you can save money, do your bit for the environment and avoid cluttering up your home. But there are also other, less visible advantages that are equally valuable.

Repair cafés and swap shops bring people together and promote the transfer of knowledge between generations. They champion exchanges of skills, materials and goodwill. Fixing, it's clear, encourages us to fix far more than just the possessions in question.

TIPS FROM GENERATIONS PAST

The constraints of rationing saw wartime men and women developing a treasure trove of tricks to help them reduce, reuse and recycle. And it wasn't just clothes! Here we share some suggestions from years past that still hold up in today's light.

- Brighten up scuffed leather shoes by scrubbing them with the cut half of a raw potato (yes, really!).
- Cut up used envelopes into small pieces, clamp the stack together with a bulldog clip, and keep on hand for when you need to write a shopping list or note.
- Tired toothbrushes and washing-up scrubbers can enjoy a second life as household cleaning tools.
- Use a water butt, or simply a large bucket, to catch rainwater for watering plants. Save cooking water, too: just leave to cool and then put to use in the garden.
- Freeze vegetable scraps to turn into homemade stock. Keeping them on ice means you can use them when you have time to make a batch of stock, reducing any waste.
- If you're a keen vegetable grower (or want to start), save loo roll tubes, fruit punnets and mushroom trays. The former are fantastic for sowing beans and peas into, and can then be planted straight into the ground, where they will quickly break down. The latter are a great size for sowing cut-and-come-again salad leaves, microgreens and cress.
- Save brown paper bags to ripen avocados, bananas and tomatoes in.

MAKE DO AND MEND, UPDATED!

The original 1943 pamphlet *Make Do and Mend*, issued by the government's Ministry of Information, focused on ways to reduce clothing waste and make the most of items that people already owned. While some of its suggestions might not sound that good to modern ears (beetroot juice as lipstick, anyone?), the fact that £140m worth of clothes in the UK end up in landfill every year* means much of its advice is more relevant than ever. We've updated some of the original tips for the modern era.

- Make a new item of clothing from something old: tired jeans with fraying hems can be cut into jean shorts, old jumpers can be turned into fingerless gloves...
- Cut up worn-out t-shirts into rectangles and use them in your household chores as polishing rags and dusters.
- If you have a wardrobe of clothes that are too big or too small, resist the temptation to throw everything out and start over. Taking in garments is easier than letting them out, but both can be done.

Look up sewing classes at your local lifelong learning centre or search for relevant tutorials on YouTube if you're not sure how to get started.

- Dropped a cup of tea on your bed sheets one too many times? Cut off the stained sections to use for cleaning purposes, and make cushion covers, handkerchiefs or table napkins out of the stain-free parts if you have access to a sewing machine.
- Clothes swapping events are now frequent occurrences in cities across the UK. If you can't find one near you, why not consider organising a similar gathering with a group of friends?
- Go on a trip to the cobbler when the soles or heels of shoes wear out, or see if you can learn to do it yourself!
- Take care of items so they last longer: follow washing instructions on the label, avoid laundering items that have only been lightly worn, and polish shoes and jewellery regularly. Washing at cooler temperatures will also extend the life of clothes.

*Statistic by WRAP.

WEBSITES
repaircafe.org.uk
libraryofthings.co.uk
therestartproject.org

Gardening in the shade

The garden is naturally a place of sunshine and shadow, of lightness and dark. Most gardeners will have shady areas of outdoor space that require a little creative planning and considered planting to look their best. With a little forethought, the dappled areas of your garden, patio or balcony can really shine – more than making up for what they lack in natural light.

Many home gardeners will have a border or bed that is shaded by a fence, wall or building. To make the most of this piece of your patch, it's vital to recognise one important fact: all shade is not created equal. Levels of shade vary in gardens, depending on the aspect, season and time of day.

All gardening necessitates an understanding of plants, their relationship to sun and shade, and an awareness of the need to plan and lay out a garden accordingly.

Putting plants that require full sun in shade, and vice-versa, will only result in wasted time and investment. Consequently, shady garden areas require shade-loving plants, but not all plants love or loathe shade to the same extent. Some can

In the past, shade gardening has been given the cold shoulder.

survive in full shade, under dense tree canopies, while others will need sunlight for at least part of the day.

In the past, shade gardening has been given the cold shoulder, with 'full sun' seen as by far the most desirable aspect in a garden. There is a sense among some that gardening in the shade is a difficult undertaking and that it is tricky to get plants to flourish in areas with little sunlight. While this may be true if you fill your shady borders with plants that would rather be drinking up the sunshine like living solar panels, a little careful consideration for a shaded area will result in an spot planted up with things suited to the setting that should well and truly prosper there.

TYPES OF SHADE

- **Light shade**: Open to the sky but not in direct sun due to a wall, fence or grouped trees.
- **Partial shade**: Gets 3-6 hours of direct sun per day in midsummer.
- **Dappled shade**: Receives diffused light through open tree canopies all day.
- **Moderate shade**: Receives 2-3 hours of direct sun per day in midsummer.
- **Deep shade**: Under dense, evergreen tree cover or overhanging buildings. If a spot receives under 2 hours of direct sunlight daily, it is also classified as deep shade.

Although shady gardens sometimes get a poor write-up, there are actually numerous positives. Garden borders in shade retain moisture much better than sunny spots and generally require less work to maintain, as weeds will grow more slowly without bright sunlight on tap. There's also an array of plants that are able to grow, indeed thrive, in shaded borders and many of these have interesting foliage that provides appeal for a long period of the year.

While sunny borders tend to peak at one point in the year, normally high summer, a shaded area can look its best for a long period due to the varying hues of green and diverse leaf shapes. Often, it will also provide interest in winter.

That's not to say there aren't plenty of fantastic flowers to appreciate on plants that prefer to sit in the shade. There's a preconception that planting for areas with lower light levels means green, silver, and yet more green. It's true that shade gardens do take advantage of eye-catching foliage, at least in part (surely that's part of the attraction!) but think of the flowers produced by hydrangeas, astrantia, astilbe, Japanese anemones, foxgloves (pictured below), hellebores… And that's to name barely a few!

EDIBLES IN THE SHADE

Most vegetable plants require full sun, but there are a few exceptions to try if your raised bed or vegetable patch only gets a few hours of sunshine each day. Most leafy edibles prefer a bit of shade (this makes them less likely to go to seed): try lettuce, Swiss chard, spinach and other leafy greens for starters. Beetroot, peas and runner beans can also tolerate gentle shade. To give the plants the best possible start, sow the seeds in modules in bright light so that the plants have a chance to develop strong root systems before being planted out.

If it's fruit you wish to grow, then your options are a little wider than when it comes to veggies. Redcurrants, gooseberries, white and blackcurrants, and raspberries all originally grew on the edges of forests so can yield satisfactory harvests in light shade. Rhubarb prefers moist soil so can also do well in partial shade, where the earth retains more moisture than full sun.

EASY UPKEEP

If you're tempted to rejig your garden layout to get rid of shady planting areas, consider how much simpler a lower-light garden can be to maintain. Weeds are slower to grow and will rarely become a nuisance. You'll have an interesting border filled with a beautiful range of foliage and flowers for longer. A shady border offers privacy, and it will look better year round.

TEN PLANTS SUITED TO A SHADY GARDEN

1 For deep shade: **Common lungwort (Pulmonaria)** makes excellent groundcover for deep shade. Its funnel-shaped flowers appear in early spring and gradually change from pink to blue in colour once they have been pollinated.

2 For low-maintenance greenery: **Ferns**. Ferns thrive in a wide variety of environments and are tolerant of a vast range of soil conditions. They are one of the oldest known plant types, having evolved beneath towering conifers during the age of the dinosaurs, so are used to indirect light and even deep shade.

3 For variety: **Coral bells (Heuchera)**. The foliage of this perennial, pictured below, is evergreen so these versatile plants provide year-round interest. Leaf colour ranges from silver to deep purple, salmon and lime green.

4 For dappled shade: **Greater masterwort (Astrantia major)**. Coming in a variety of colours ranging from deep crimson to pale pink and white, astrantia has a similar look to sun-lover scabious but thrives in light, dappled shade due to its woodland origins. It will readily self-seed around the garden – an added bonus!

5 For under trees: **Primroses (Primula vulgaris)**. This low, carpet-spreading perennial flower is native to British woodlands and does best in damp, dappled shade. They will also spread widely and provide a welcome burst of lightness in shade beneath trees in early spring.

6 For ground cover: **Periwinkle (Vinca)**. The periwinkle plant is part of the violet family and provides good winter colour and satisfying ground cover. It is handy for out-competing weeds in wilder areas of your garden.

7 For interesting foliage: **Siberian bugloss (Brunnera macrophylla)**. In spring, these plants throw up a profusion of small, pale blue flowers – very similar in appearance to forget-me-nots – while their leaves are dotted with silvery veins.

8 For flowers: **Hydrangeas (Hydrangea macrophylla, petiolaris** and **arborescens)**. Once established, these shrubs will provide reliable summer colour beneath trees or on the shady side of a garden. Tough and resilient, they come in a variety of sizes and different forms, including climbers. They also provide near year-round interest as their brown seed heads should not be cut down until spring.

9 For structural interest: **Japanese aralia (Fatsia japonica)**. This broadleaf evergreen plant has intriguing star-shaped leaves and umbels of white flowerheads in autumn. It will thrive even in the full shade that kills off many other plants. It can grow up to 2.5 metres (8 feet) tall so is ideal for the back of a shaded border, but also does well in containers.

10 For cottage gardens: **Foxgloves (Digitalis)**. Foxglove spires are at home in any cottage garden and are ideal for providing colour in early to mid-summer. When choosing where to plant, keep in mind that foxgloves (both flower and foliage) are toxic to humans and pets if ingested.

WEBSITES
plantsforshade.co.uk
rhs.org.uk
kew.org
gardenersworld.com

The pleasure of pies

Steak and ale, chicken and mushroom, banoffee, apple, cheese and onion...
A pie by any other name tends to taste just as good! This list of popular
British pies is far from exhaustive, and shows that this pastry
provision is a rightful staple of the country's cuisine.

The Romans brought many things to Britain, not least roads and running water, but they can also be credited with ferrying the humble pie to these island shores. Their actions still reverberate through the generations: today 75% of Brits eat a pie at least once a month and the average British person can expect to enjoy 2,160 pies in their lifetime*.

The Egyptians were the first to cook pies like those we eat today.

Despite the Roman roots of pies in Britain, the ancient Egyptians are thought to have been the first to cook pies like the ones we eat today. A recipe for a chicken version was discovered carved onto a tablet traced back to Mesopotamia around 2,000 BC.

The crust of these early pies was thought to have been made from a mixture of ground oats and wheat, often filled with honey.

Pies of past and present are as diverse as the people who have cooked them throughout history. A pie is usually defined as a baked dish containing fruit, meat or vegetables, with a base, sides and lid made of pastry. Despite this general definition, pies can be open or closed; sweet, savoury or both; and vary in size from small hand pies (so named because they can be held in one's fingers) to platter-sized apple tarts baked to serve a hungry crowd.

*Statistic by JusRol

BY ANOTHER NAME

The word pie – spelled 'pye' in medieval English – first appeared in relation to food in 1303. In 1362 Chaucer mentioned the word in *The Canterbury Tales*, a sure sign that the noun was in wide enough use to be understood by the literate population. The name is likely linked to the word 'magpie': pies of that era were generally filled with a diverse array of ingredients (whatever was to hand or available), the various combinations of fillings being likened to the miscellany of objects collected by the covetous garden birds.

Pies were a useful way for medieval cooks to use up odds and ends of meat or vegetables. But the pastry crust also served another functional purpose: the thick exterior provided a handy means of preserving meat, both at home and on long voyages at sea. The outer pastry layer was often inedible, having been cooked for hours, and served more as a kind of crude food storage than a delicious part of the pie in its own right. Historians believe that the tough crusts were sometimes fed to unlucky kitchen servants.

SWEET AND SAVOURY

By the mid-17th century, pies were well-established in England, with both meat and fruit pies common. Sweet and savoury fillings were often combined under the same lid of pastry – the most famous under this heading is the beloved mince pie. While mince pies no longer contain meat, the name hints at the festive snack's sweet and sour origins: the original mince pies of Tudor times contained shredded meat, suet and dried fruit. European crusaders brought this unexpected combination of ingredients back from the Holy Land, where cooking methods often united meat, fruit and spices.

UNEXPECTED FILLINGS

Around this time, so-named 'surprise pies' were a recurring feature at feasts hosted by the Tudor and Stuart monarchs. Such dishes often contained live birds, crammed into a pastry dome on top of the pie (added after it was baked, to ensure their survival). They would fly out of the top and into the rafters when the pie was cut into, providing lively entertainment for dinner guests.

These odd dishes are likely the origin of the nursery rhyme 'Sing a Song of Sixpence' which contains the line 'four-and-twenty blackbirds

PASTRY A-PLENTY

At its most elemental, pastry is a mixture of flour, water and fat. There are five basic types of pastry: shortcrust, filo, choux, rough puff and puff. Many pastries are made with shortening, a fat product that is solid at room temperature. Its composition is ideal for creating crumbly crusts. There's an old saying that cold hands make good pastry and though it sounds like hearsay, it's the truth! Cool hands are less likely to melt the butter, so remember to run your palms under the cold tap before you begin making your own pie crust.

baked in a pie'. Surprise contents were not limited to garden birds though; other shock attractions included frogs, squirrels and even foxes!

While the ancient Egyptians, Greeks and Romans would have used olive oil as the primary fat in their approximations of pies due to its wide availability, Europeans began using butter, lard or suet in their pastry in the Middle Ages. Eventually, this led to softer, more pliable crusts and is probably when edible pastry cases became more common.

STREET FOOD

In Victorian times pies were a popular street food, often hawked by piemen who walked the streets selling their creations from small, portable ovens (lacking the funds to set up shop in a more permanent fashion). Meat and fruit fillings were common, but the most prevalent filling was something very much of its time: eel.

Eels were one of very few fish that could survive in the heavily polluted waterways of Victorian Britain and were therefore cheaply and widely available. It was around this time that 'pie and mash' became the classic combination that endures to this day. Mashed potatoes were an inclusion used to bulk out the dish to satisfy hungry workers.

While pies were traditionally filled with meat, today pies are perhaps just as likely to be vegetarian. The traditional Cornish pasty is crammed with beef, turnips or swede, potato and onion, but outside Cornwall, you're just as likely to find pasties filled with cheese and onion, curried cauliflower, even spinach and ricotta.

But when push comes to shove, it seems that meaty pies remain the apple of this country's eye. A 2019 study conducted by Charlie Bigham's found that steak and kidney pie topped the charts as the UK's most popular savoury pie. This traditional British concoction is a long-standing pub favourite stuffed with diced steak, onion, and kidney cooked in gravy. It is thought to date back to the 19th century, when it was more common to use all parts of an animal.

GLOBAL PHENOMENON

It's not just in Britain that the humble pie is a staple of national cuisine. America is widely associated with apple pie, although it was European pilgrims who first brought both the recipe and the apples to the USA. Now the dish is such an American symbol, there is even a saying that honours it: 'As American as apple pie'.

Savoury pies are also enjoyed throughout the world. In Europe alone, examples include *spanakopita*, a Greek pie made with flaky filo pastry and filled with spinach and Feta cheese, and *coulibiac*, a pie native to Russia filled with rice, salmon, mushrooms and hard-boiled eggs. Wherever you are and whatever your tastes, it would seem there really is a pie for everyone.

3 VERY BRITISH PIES

Melton Mowbray pork pies
The gold standard of pork pies, the Melton Mowbray pork pie comes from the Leicestershire town of the same name. Unlike other pork pies, the meat is chopped rather than minced and the pie crust is formed by hand. Melton Mowbray pies are also served cold, unlike the Yorkshire pork pie. They are now a protected product, so only those produced in the town can market themselves as Melton Mowbray pork pies.

Stargazy pie
Stargazy pie is a Cornish dish made of baked pilchards, eggs and potatoes covered with a pastry crust. The eponymous feature of stargazy pie is the fish heads poking through the crust – they appear to be gazing upwards at the sky.

Welsh oggie
The Welsh oggie, little known outside Wales itself, is the country's version of the Cornish pasty. It is cooked with Welsh lamb, leeks (what else!) and potatoes. Like the Cornish pasty, it was the meal of choice for tin miners who could not return home for lunch, so required a filling, portable lunch to eat below ground.
Find two more British pie recipes on the following page.

CUMBERLAND RUM NICKY

Stoned dates 225g (8oz), chopped
Ready-to-eat dried apricots 110g (4oz), chopped
Chopped glacé ginger 50g (2oz)
Light rum 3 tbsp
Orange 1, juice only
Soft light brown sugar 2 tbsp
Plain flour 225g (8oz)
Butter 125g (4½oz)
Egg yolk 1, lightly beaten
Milk 1 tbsp

1 Preheat oven to 200°C/180°fan/Gas 6. Mix dates, apricots, ginger, rum and orange juice together with half the sugar. Leave to soak while making the pastry.
2 Put flour, a pinch of salt and 110g (4oz) butter in a bowl. Rub in until mixture resembles fine breadcrumbs. Add remaining sugar, egg yolk and 2 tbsp water to bind.
3 Knead pastry on a floured surface. Roll out half and use to line a greased 25cm (10in) flat pie plate.
4 Spread fruit mixture over pastry and dot with remaining butter. Brush edge with a little water.
5 Roll out remaining pastry. Use to cover the pie. Make a hole in the centre to allow steam to escape. Brush with milk and bake for 30-35 minutes.

Serves 6 • Time 50 mins
Calories 502 • Fibre 5.5g • Salt 0.1g • Sugar 5.8g
Fat 21.2g of which 12.2g is saturated

HUNTINGDON FIDGET PIE

Plain flour 275g (10oz)
Butter 125g (4½oz), diced
Rindless bacon 250g (9oz), roughly chopped
Onion 1, peeled and roughly chopped
Cooking apples 2, peeled, cored and chopped
Chopped fresh parsley 4 tsp
Medium dry cider 150ml (¼ pint)
Chicken stock 150ml (¼ pint)
Egg 1, beaten

1 Preheat oven to 190°C/170°fan/Gas 5. Sift 250g (9oz) flour and a pinch salt into a large bowl. Add butter and rub in until breadcrumbs. Stir in 2-3 tbsp cold water for a firm dough. Knead lightly, then wrap in foil and chill.
2 Combine bacon, onion and apples and divide between 4 x 400ml (14fl oz) pie dishes. Add parsley; season.
3 Put remaining flour in a bowl and add cider and stock gradually, mixing well. Pour mixture into pie dishes.
4 Roll out pastry onto a floured surface. Cut out strips long enough to cover rims of dishes. Moisten rims with water, place strips on rims and press down. Cut circles of pastry to form lids. Moisten strips, put lids on top, trim off excess and press to seal. Cut a cross in centre of each and fold pastry back to show a square of filling.
5 Brush pastry with beaten egg, then bake in the oven for 30 minutes, until golden and the filling is cooked.

Makes 4 pies • Time 45 mins
Calories 604 • Fibre 4.4g • Salt 1.8g • Sugar 0.5g
Fat 32.2g of which 18.5g is saturated

Cook's information

DRY WEIGHT CONVERSIONS

grams (g)	ounces (oz)
15	½
25	1
50	2
75	3
110	4 (¼lb)
150	5
175	6
200	7
225	8 (½lb)
250	9
275	10
300	11
350	12 (¾lb)
375	13
400	14
425	15
450	16 (1lb)
500	1lb 2oz
680	1½lb
750	1lb 10oz
900	2lb

These quantities are not exact, but they have been calculated to give proportionately correct measurements.

SPOON MEASURES

1 tablespoon	=	3 level teaspoons
1 level tablespoon	=	15ml
1 level teaspoon	=	5ml
If greater accuracy is not required:		
1 rounded teaspoon	=	2 level teaspoons
1 heaped teaspoon	=	3 level teaspoons or 1 level tablespoon

LIQUID CONVERSIONS

millilitres (ml)	fluid ounces (fl oz)	US cups
15	½	1 tbsp (level)
30	1	⅛
60	2	¼
90	3	⅜
125	4	½
150	5 (¼ pint)	⅔
175	6	¾
225	8	1
300	10 (½ pint)	1¼
350	12	1½
450	16	2
500	18	2¼
600	20 (1 pint)	2½
900	1½ pints	3¾
1 litre	1¾ pints	1 quart (4 cups)
1.25 litres	2 pints	1¼ quarts
1.5 litres	2½ pints	3 US pints
2 litres	3½ pints	2 quarts

These quantities are not exact, but they have been calculated to give proportionately correct measurements.

REFERENCE INTAKE (RI)

Energy (calories)	2,000
Fat (g)	<70
of which saturates (g)	<20
Carbohydrate (g)	260
of which total sugars (g)	90
Protein (g)	50
Salt (g)	<6

These amounts indicate an adult's daily requirements for a healthy, balanced diet.

GRILLING TIMES: FISH

	minutes each side
Cod (steak)	5–6
Dover sole (fillet)	2–3
Halibut (steak)	5–6
Herring (whole)	4–5
Mackerel (whole)	6–7
Monkfish (steak)	5–6
Plaice (whole)	4–6
Plaice (fillet)	2–3
Salmon (steak)	5–6
Skate	5–6
Tuna (steak)	1–2

Times given for fish weighing approximately 175–225g (6–8oz).

OVEN TEMPERATURES

°C	(fan)	°F	gas	description
110	(90)	225	¼	cool
120/130	(100/110)	250	½	cool
140	(120)	275	1	very low
150	(130)	300	2	very low
160/170	(140/150)	325	3	low to moderate
180	(160)	350	4	moderate
190	(170)	375	5	moderately hot
200	(180)	400	6	hot
220	(200)	425	7	hot
230	(210)	450	8	hot
240	(220)	475	9	very hot

Guide to recommended equivalent settings, not exact conversions. Always refer to your cooker instruction book.

ROASTING TIMES: MEAT*

Set oven temperature to 180°C/160°fan/Gas 4.

	cooking time per 450g/1lb	extra cooking time
Beef		
rare	20 min	20 min
medium	25 min	25 min
well done	30 min	30 min
Lamb		
medium	25 min	25 min
well done	30 min	30 min
Pork		
medium	30 min	30 min
well done	35 min	35 min

Let the cooked meat rest for 5–15 minutes before carving to allow the juices to be reabsorbed and to make carving easier.

STEAMING TIMES: VEGETABLES

	minutes
Asparagus	5–7
Beansprouts	3–4
Beetroot (sliced)	5–7
Broccoli (florets)	5–7
Brussels sprouts	5–7
Cabbage (chopped)	4–6
Carrots (thickly sliced)	5–7
Cauliflower (florets)	5–7
Courgettes (sliced)	3–5
Green beans	5–7
Leeks	5–8
Mangetout peas	3–5
Peas	3–5
Potatoes (cubed)	5–7

Times given are for steaming from when water has started to boil.

ROASTING TIMES: POULTRY*

	oven temperature	cooking time per 450g/1lb	extra cooking time	resting time
Chicken	220°C/200°fan/Gas 7 for 20 min; then 190°C/170°fan/Gas 5	20 min	20 min	15 min
Turkey (stuffed weight)	220°C/200°fan/Gas 7 uncovered for 30 min; then, covered, 190°C/170°fan/Gas 5; then for last 30 min, uncovered, 200°C/180°fan/Gas 6	18 min	18 min	30 min
Duck	230°C/210°fan/Gas 8 for 20 min; then 180°C/160°fan/Gas 4	15 min	—	15 min

*Note that for fan ovens, cooking times are generally reduced by 10 minutes for every hour. These timings and oven temperatures are guidelines – follow instructions on packaging if possible.

How to get your 5 a day

A balanced diet contains at least five different portions of fruit and vegetables a day and a good mix throughout the week.

Sometimes eating healthily can feel like a minefield in the face of so much conflicting advice. Still, we all know eating enough fruit and veg is crucial for good health. It needn't be confusing: at its best, getting your 5 a day can be simple and delicious. Each number below represents 1 of your 5 a day.

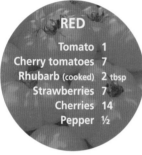

RED
Tomato	1
Cherry tomatoes	7
Rhubarb (cooked)	2 tbsp
Strawberries	7
Cherries	14
Pepper	½

ORANGE
Orange	1
Nectarine	1
Apricots	3
Carrots	3 tbsp
Baked beans	3 tbsp
Sweet potato	1

YELLOW
Banana	1
Grapefruit	½
Pineapple	1 slice
Sweetcorn	3 tbsp
Yellow lentils	3 tbsp
Chickpeas	3 tbsp

GREEN
Apple	1
Melon	1 slice
Lettuce	1 bowl
Peas	3 tbsp
Green beans	4 tbsp
Avocado	½

PURPLE
Plums	2
Blackcurrants	4 tbsp
Sultanas	1 tbsp
Kidney beans	3 tbsp
Beetroot	7 slices
Aubergine	½

WHITE
Leek	1
Cauliflower	8 florets
Mushrooms (chopped)	3 tbsp
Turnip/swede	3 tbsp
Butter beans	3 tbsp
Parsnip	1

EAT THE RAINBOW

Try to choose each portion from a different colour group. Aiming for a colourful plate can be a simple way to get the full range of vitamins and minerals your body needs. And your meals will be beautiful, too!

WHAT COUNTS?

Almost all fruits and vegetables count towards your 5 a day. This includes fresh produce, frozen, tinned and preserved fruits and vegetables.

One portion of your 5 a day...
= 80g of fruit
= 80g of vegetables
= 30g dried fruit

DID YOU KNOW...?

Mixing fruits or vegetables (e.g. 40g banana and 40g strawberries) still counts towards your total as long as each portion adds up to 80g.

Fruit juices and smoothies only count as one portion, no matter how many glasses you drink. The NHS recommends no more than 150ml a day.

Pulses, beans and legumes, like lentils, kidney beans or chickpeas, only count as one portion of your 5 a day, regardless of how many 80g portions you eat.

Potatoes don't count towards your 5 a day because of their high starch content, but they are still a great source of fibre, potassium and B vitamins. However, sweet potatoes do count.

Washing instructions

TEXTILE CYCLES

Check both the temperature, given by the figure in the tub, and the machine-action, shown by the bar(s) under it. The temperature may be indicated by dots (six for 95°, four for 60°, two for 40° and one for 30°).

 Maximum agitation. Cotton cycle
White cotton or linen articles without special finishes.

 Maximum agitation. Cotton cycle
Cotton or linen articles without special finishes where colours are fast at 60°C.

 Maximum agitation. Cotton cycle
Cotton or linen where colours are fast at 40°C but not at 60°C.

 Medium agitation. Synthetic cycle
Acrylics, acetate or triacetate, including mixtures with wool, polyester and wool blends.

 Minimum agitation. Wool cycle
Wool, including blankets, wool mixed with other fibres, viscose and silk.

 Gentle agitation. Delicates cycle
Silk, acetates and mixed synthetics not colourfast at 40°C.

 Hand wash only
See garment label for further instructions.

 Do not machine or hand wash

DRY-CLEANING

The letter P or F indicates the cleaning fluids that may be used by your professional dry-cleaner.

 May be dry-cleaned

 Do not dry-clean

BLEACHING

 Bleach may be used

 Do not bleach

 Do not use chlorine bleach

DRYING SYMBOLS

Check the label to see if your garment can be tumble-dried. The label may advise using a reduced heat setting by putting a single dot within the circle. Two dots indicate a higher heat setting.

 May be tumble-dried

 Do not tumble-dry

 Hang dry

 Drip dry recommended

 Dry flat

IRONING

- The dots inside the iron indicate the temperature setting. One dot represents the coolest setting and three dots are for the hottest temperature. The table (right) is a guide to the temperature to use for specific types of fabric.
- You should always use the setting recommended by the manufacturer. For some materials the advice may be that you iron on the wrong side of the fabric only, so check the label.
- To avoid creases, store your clothes in drawers and wardrobes loosely; don't pack them in.

 Hot (3 dots)
Cotton and linen fabrics.

 Warm (2 dots)
Polyester mixtures and wool.

 Cool (1 dot)
Acrylic, nylon, acetate, triacetate, viscose and polyester.

 Do not iron

ECO LAUNDRY

To limit the environmental impact of laundry, wash garments sparingly. Launder only if they look or smell dirty and try to wash at 30°C.

Stain removal

The most important factor in attacking stains is to act swiftly. The newer the stain, whether greasy, non-greasy, or a combination of the two, the easier it will be to remove without damage.

First and foremost, check what processes and cleaning agents are suitable for the stained item. Wool and silk often need to be treated differently from cotton and synthetics, for example. Always check care labels if possible, and follow what they say.

Likewise, bear in mind that whites may need to be treated differently from coloureds. In any case, always check for colourfastness before soaking.

Biological detergent works well even at low temperatures due to the enzymes it contains.

Whenever you can, use it for stain removal but don't use it, or any other enzyme-based cleaner, on wool or silk. For hand-washing, old or delicate fabrics and baby clothes, use a mild non-biological detergent.

Some of the cleaning agents you will need contain chemicals that are poisonous or flammable. Always read the packaging carefully and store them away from children.

For your safety, work in an area that has plenty of ventilation.

CLEANING KIT

Bicarbonate of soda: Use this – or cornflour or talcum powder – to absorb grease and oil.

Borax: Boosts your detergent's performance.

Detergents: Biological/non-biological/heavy-duty/mild. Liquid detergent is good for oily stains and as a pre-wash treatment.

Eucalyptus oil: Available from major chemists. Good for treating greasy stains.

Glycerine: For treating old stains before washing.

Hydrogen peroxide: Ask your chemist for 3%, which is 10 volume strength (VS). Don't use on wool or silk.

Methylated spirits: From DIY stores. Apply with cotton buds. Don't use on fabric that contains acetate or triacetate.

Pre-wash treatments: Some are for common stains, some are more specific. Follow the manufacturer's instructions.

White distilled vinegar: Use as a solution of 15ml vinegar to 300ml water (3 tsp to ½ pint); or mixed to a paste with bicarbonate of soda.

White spirit: Available from DIY stores. Good for treating paint and grease stains.

PERSONAL

Blood: Soak in cold water with biological detergent or salt; or rub in a paste of bicarb and cold water, leave to dry, brush off. Wash in biological detergent (if appropriate for the fabric).

Make-up: Work in biological liquid detergent; wash as usual.

Perspiration: Sponge with white vinegar, rinse and soak in salt solution or biological detergent. Soften old stains with glycerine. Rinse, wash as usual.

Urine: Rinse in cold water; dab with hydrogen peroxide, or soak in biological detergent; rinse, wash as usual. For pet urine, soak in soda water, blot excess, sponge with salty water, rinse and blot dry. Sprinkle with bicarb, leave for a while, then vacuum.

Vomit: Rinse under running cold water; soak in a sterilising solution, or biological detergent with some disinfectant added; wash as usual.

FOOD AND DRINKS

Chocolate: Rinse in cold water; apply biological detergent and soak overnight if necessary; wash in suitable detergent.

Coffee: Soak in lukewarm water, use a pre-wash treatment and wash in suitable detergent.

Egg: Dab with cold salty water; wash in biological detergent.

Gravy: Soak in cold water with biological detergent; usual wash.

Grease: Cover with bicarb, leave for an hour; brush off.

WHAT TO DO

• Remove any solids with a blunt knife, and blot liquids with white kitchen paper.

• Apply stain remover to a small, unseen area and wait 5–10 minutes. If the fabric reacts, or if in doubt, seek dry-cleaning advice. Avoid treating delicate or expensive fabrics, or those that require dry-cleaning only.

Soak in liquid detergent and wash in water as hot as the fabric allows.

Milk and fruit juice: Rinse under running cold water, then soak in biological detergent and wash in water as hot as the fabric allows.

Oil/salad dressings: Blot and dab with biological liquid detergent; or sprinkle with bicarb, brush off and soak in washing-up liquid. Usual wash.

Tea: Treat as coffee but wash in heavy-duty detergent; or dab with lemon juice, rinse and wash in biological detergent; or pour white vinegar solution, leave for 10 mins and wash.

Tomato sauce: Dab gently with biological liquid detergent and wash as usual; or rinse in cold water, dab with white vinegar, rinse and wash as usual.

Wine, red: Pour soda water over the stain, blot, cover with salt and leave for 30 minutes. Soak in cold water; sponge with biological detergent and wash as usual. On upholstery and carpets, cover with salt, leave to absorb and brush off. Dab with warm water and biological detergent; then with cold water.

Wine, white: Rinse in warm water; dab with biological liquid

• Don't over-soak the fabric with a cleaning agent. To avoid making a ring mark, use a soft, absorbent cloth to apply the cleaning agent and work in a circular motion from the outside inwards. Dab, rather than rub, because rubbing can damage the fabric and it can also spread the stain.

detergent (white vinegar for silk and wool). Rinse and wash as usual. On upholstery and carpets, blot then sponge gently with soapy water (do not rub).

MISCELLANEOUS

Grass: Dab with methylated spirits; rinse with warm soapy water. Use an appropriate pre-wash treatment and then wash in heavy-duty detergent.

Ink (ballpoint or felt tip): Dab with diluted methylated spirits; rinse and sponge with biological detergent; wash as usual. If persistent, treat as rust.

Rust: Dab with lemon juice, cover with salt, leave for at least an hour; rinse; usual wash.

Suntan lotion: Use a pre-wash for greasy stains, or treat with eucalyptus oil or a product for removing hard-water stains. Wash in biological detergent.

Tar: Dab with eucalyptus oil on reverse of fabric; wash in biological detergent in water as hot as fabric allows.

Metric conversions

			To convert	multiply by
Length				
1 millimetre (mm)		= 0.0394in	mm to in	0.0394
1 centimetre (cm)	= 10mm	= 0.394in	cm to in	0.394
1 metre (m)	= 100cm	= 1.09yd	m to yd	1.09
1 kilometre (km)	= 1000m	= 0.621 mile	km to mi	0.621
1 inch (in)		= 2.54cm	in to cm	2.54
1 foot (ft)	= 12in	= 30.5cm	ft to cm	30.5
1 yard (yd)	= 3ft	= 0.914m	yd to m	0.914
1 mile (mi)	= 1760yd	= 1.61km	mi to km	1.61
Area				
1 sq millimetre (mm)		= 0.00155sq in	mm^2 to in^2	0.00155
1 sq centimetre (cm)	= 100sq mm	= 0.155sq in	cm^2 to in^2	0.155
1 sq metre (m)	= 10,000sq cm	= 1.2sq yd	m^2 to yd^2	1.2
1 hectare (ha)	= 10,000sq m	= 2.47a	ha to a	2.47
1 sq kilometre (km)	= 100ha	= 0.386sq mile	km^2 to mi^2	0.386
1 sq inch (in)		= 6.45sq cm	in^2 to cm^2	6.45
1 sq foot (ft)	= 144sq in	= 0.0929sq m	ft^2 to m^2	0.0929
1 sq yard (yd)	= 9sq ft	= 0.836sq m	yd^2 to m^2	0.836
1 acre (a)	= 4840sq yd	= 4047sq m	a to m^2	4047
1 sq mile (mi)	= 640a	= 2.59sq km	mi^2 to km^2	2.59
Volume				
1 cu centimetre (cm)	= 1000cu mm	= 0.0611cu in	cm^3 to in^3	0.0611
1 cu decimetre (dm)	= 1000cu cm	= 0.0353cu ft	dm^3 to ft^3	0.0353
1 cu metre (m)	= 1000cu dm	= 1.31cu yd	m^3 to yd^3	1.31
1 cu inch (in)		= 16.4cu cm	in^3 to cm^3	16.4
1 cu foot (ft)	= 1730cu in	= 28.4cu dm	ft^3 to dm^3	28.4
1 cu yard (yd)	= 27cu ft	= 0.765cu m	yd^3 to m^3	0.765
Capacity				
1 millilitre (ml)		= 0.0352fl oz	ml to fl oz	0.0352
1 centilitre (cl)	= 10ml	= 0.352fl oz	cl to fl oz	0.352
1 litre (l)	= 100cl	= 1.76pt	l to pt	1.76
1 fluid ounce (fl oz)		= 28.4ml	fl oz to ml	28.4
1 gill (gi)	= 5fl oz	= 14.2cl	gi to cl	14.2
1 pint (pt)	= 20fl oz	= 0.568l	pt to l	0.568
1 quart (qt)	= 2pt	= 1.14l	qt to l	1.14
1 gallon (gal)	= 4qt	= 4.55l	gal to l	4.55
Weight				
1 gram (g)	= 1000mg	= 0.0353oz	g to oz	0.0353
1 kilogram (kg)	= 1000g	= 2.2lb	kg to lb	2.2
1 tonne (t)	= 1000kg	= 0.984 ton	tonne to ton	0.984
1 ounce (oz)	= 438 grains	= 28.3g	oz to g	28.3
1 pound (lb)	= 16oz	= 0.454kg	lb to kg	0.454
1 stone (st)	= 14lb	= 6.35kg	st to kg	6.35
1 ton (t)	= 160st	= 1.02 tonne	ton to tonne	1.02

2022

27 Monday
☾ Last quarter
Bank Holiday, UK

28 Tuesday
Bank Holiday, UK

29 Wednesday

30 Thursday

31 Friday
New Year's Eve

REMINDERS

HOT CHEDDAR RAREBIT DIP

Double cream 275ml (9fl oz)
Dijon mustard 1½ tsp
Tamarind paste 1 tsp (optional)
Soy sauce 1 tbsp
Brown ale 90ml (3fl oz)
Mature Cheddar cheese 250g (9oz), grated
Plain flour 1 tbsp
Toasted baguette and vegetable crudités to serve

1 Pour cream into a pan and add mustard, tamarind paste, if using, soy and brown ale.
2 Heat gently, whisking, for about 5 minutes until ingredients are combined.
3 Season, add grated cheese and flour, and whisk for a further 2-3 minutes, until thickened and smooth.
4 Spoon into a shallow bowl and serve immediately with toasted baguette and vegetable crudités.

Serves 4 • Time 15 mins
Calories 637 • Fibre 0.4g • Salt 1.8g • Sugar 0.1g
Fat 59.2g of which 36.6g is saturated

55

3   Monday
Bank Holiday, UK

4   Tuesday
Bank Holiday, Scotland

5   Wednesday

6   Thursday
Epiphany

7   Friday

REMINDERS

Saturday 8

Sunday 9
) First quarter

BUTTERY CHILLI PRAWN LINGUINE

Linguine 150g (5oz)
Olive oil 1 tbsp
Butter 25g (1oz)
Garlic 1 clove, peeled and finely chopped
Chilli flakes ¼ tsp
Chorizo 25g (1oz), sliced (optional)
Lemon 1, finely grated zest
Cooked prawns 150g (5oz)
Salad tomatoes 2, diced
Chopped fresh parsley or basil to serve
(optional)

1 Place linguine in a pan of boiling water and cook according to the packet instructions.
2 Meanwhile, put oil, butter, garlic, chilli flakes and chorizo, if using, into a frying pan over a medium heat. Cook for about 3 minutes, stirring.
3 Add lemon zest, prawns and tomatoes and cook for a further 3 minutes or until prawns are hot.
4 Drain linguine and divide between two pasta bowls. Top with prawn mixture and sprinkle with chopped herbs, if using.

Serves 2 • Time 10 mins
Calories 512 • Fibre 5.2g • Salt 1.8g • Sugar 0g
Fat 21.4g of which 9.1g is saturated

10 Monday

11 Tuesday

12 Wednesday

13 Thursday

14 Friday

REMINDERS

Sunday 16

PIZZA SCONES

Self-raising flour 300g (11oz)
Baking powder 1 tsp
Butter or margarine 65g (2½oz)
Italian hard cheese 75g (3oz), grated
Dry pack sundried tomatoes 50g (2oz),
finely chopped
Dried oregano 1 tbsp
Passata 100ml (3½fl oz)
Cheddar cheese 75g (3oz), grated
Large ripe tomato 1, thinly sliced
Pitted black olives 4, halved

1 Preheat oven to 200°C/180°fan/Gas 6. Line
2 baking trays with baking paper. Sift flour and
baking powder into a bowl and rub in butter or
margarine with your fingertips until well combined.
2 Mix in Italian cheese, dried tomatoes and oregano.
Make a well in centre. Put passata in a jug and make
up to 200ml (7fl oz) with cold water. Gradually stir in
enough tomato liquid to form a soft dough. Turn out
onto a lightly floured surface and knead until smooth.
3 Divide dough into 8 equal pieces and form each
into a 9cm (3½in) round. Arrange on trays and bake
for 15-20 minutes. Sprinkle with Cheddar and top
with a slice of tomato. Return to oven for a further 10
minutes until risen and golden. Cool on a wire rack.
Once cooled, season and top each with an olive half.
TIP Serve warm or cold with coleslaw and salad for
a light meal, or split and fill with salad for a picnic.

Makes 8 • Time 50 mins
Calories 310 • Fibre 2.2g • Salt 1.1g • Sugar 0.8g
Fat 16.8g of which 8.7g is saturated

59

17 Monday
○ Full moon

18 Tuesday

19 Wednesday

20 Thursday

21 Friday

REMINDERS

Sunday 23

GLUTEN-FREE BAKEWELL BLONDIES

Lightly salted butter 75g (3oz), plus extra for greasing
White chocolate chips 100g (3½oz)
Medium eggs 2
Caster sugar 75g (3oz)
Gluten-free self-raising flour 75g (3oz)
Ground almonds 75g (3oz)
Glacé cherries 75g (3oz), chopped
Natural almond extract 1 tsp
Raspberry jam 2 tbsp
Flaked almonds 25g (1oz)
Vanilla ice cream to serve (optional)

1 Preheat oven to 200°C/180°fan/Gas 6. Grease and line an 18cm (7in) square cake tin.
2 Put chocolate chips in a pan with butter and heat very gently until melted.
3 Meanwhile, break eggs into a bowl. Stir in sugar, then sift in flour and add ground almonds. Stir in cherries, almond extract and melted white chocolate until well combined.
4 Spoon into prepared tin and smooth top. Stir jam to soften, then drizzle over top of mixture and gently swirl in with a knife. Sprinkle with flaked almonds and bake for 20 minutes until risen and lightly golden on top.
5 Leave to cool in tin for 5 minutes, then cut into nine pieces and serve hot with scoops of vanilla ice cream, if you like, or eat cold.

TIP Gluten-free flour gives a denser texture, but you can use plain wheat flour if preferred.

Makes 9 • Time 30 mins
Calories 304 • Fibre 0.5g • Salt 0.2g • Sugar 23.2g
Fat 17.6g of which 7.2g is saturated

24 Monday

25 Tuesday
Burns Night
(Last quarter

26 Wednesday

27 Thursday

28 Friday

REMINDERS

Saturday 29

Sunday 30

HAGGIS WITH SCALLOPS, APPLE & WHISKY SAUCE

Celeriac 1, peeled and cut into small chunks
Double cream 4 tbsp
Haggis 2 x 227g 'sausage-shaped' packs
Olive oil 1 tbsp
Butter 25g (1oz)
Queen scallops 12
Dessert apple 1, cored, quartered and each wedge cut into 5 slices
Scottish honey 1 tbsp
Cider vinegar 2 tbsp
Whisky 4 tbsp
Dijon mustard 2 tsp

1 Put celeriac in a pan, cover with cold water, bring to boil and simmer for 20 minutes or until tender. Drain, dry off in a pan, transfer to a food processor and whizz until smooth, adding cream gradually. Season.
2 Meanwhile, slice each haggis into 10 rounds. Heat oil in a frying pan, add haggis and cook over a low heat for 3 minutes, then flip slices and cook for 2 minutes until crispy. Remove from pan to a warm oven. Wipe pan with kitchen paper. Add butter to pan, increase heat, add scallops and cook for 1½ minutes each side. Remove from pan with a slotted spoon and put in oven.
3 Add apple to pan, cook until coloured. Add honey and cook until caramelised. Stir in vinegar, whisky and mustard; heat through to make a glossy sauce.
4 Spoon purée onto hot plates. Arrange haggis on top, then scallops and apple and spoon sauce over.

Serves 4 • Time 30 mins
Calories 616 • Fibre 2.4g • Salt 2.4g • Sugar 4.6g
Fat 45.7g of which 20.9g is saturated

31 Monday

1 Tuesday FEBRUARY
Chinese New Year
● New moon

2 Wednesday

3 Thursday

4 Friday

REMINDERS

Saturday 5

Sunday 6
Accession of Queen Elizabeth II

DHAL WITH PANEER

Small onion 1, peeled and chopped
Rapeseed oil 1 tbsp
Garlic 2 cloves, peeled and thinly sliced
Tikka curry paste 2 tbsp
Split red lentils 75g (3oz), rinsed
Baby leaf greens 200g (7oz), rinsed and drained
Paneer cheese 75g (3oz), cut into 8 cubes
**Freeze-fried curry leaves or fresh coriander
leaves** 1 tbsp, plus extra coriander to garnish
(optional)
Natural yogurt and naan breads to serve (optional)

1 Put onion and 2 teaspoons oil in a large pan over a
medium heat, cover and cook for 5 minutes. Stir in half
the garlic along with curry paste and cook for 1 minute.
2 Add lentils, pour in 600ml (1 pint) boiling water and
simmer, uncovered, for 12 minutes until lentils are
just tender.
3 Meanwhile, cut out thick stems and veins of greens
using scissors. Cut leaves into fine strips.
4 Heat remaining oil in a nonstick frying pan over a
high heat. Fry paneer for a couple of minutes, turning
occasionally, until golden. Add curry leaves or coriander
and remaining garlic; cook for another minute.
5 Add greens to lentils and cook until they just begin
to wilt. Season to taste. Serve lentil dhal with paneer
cubes sprinkled over and garnish with coriander
leaves, if using. Serve with natural yogurt and naan
breads, if you like.
TIPS Freeze-dried curry leaves can be found in the
supermarket spices aisle. Halloumi works as an
alternative to paneer.

Serves 2 • Time 30 mins
Calories 369 kcal • Fibre 5.6g • Salt 0.9g • Sugar 0g
Fat 19.9g of which 6.3g is saturated

7   Monday

8   Tuesday
) First quarter

9   Wednesday

10 Thursday

11 Friday

REMINDERS

BEEF FAJITAS WITH SWEETCORN SALSA

Thin cut beef steaks 450g (1lb), cut into strips
Red, yellow and green pepper ½ each, deseeded, cored and cut into thin strips
Small onion 1, peeled and sliced
Garlic cloves 2, peeled and finely chopped
Fajita seasoning 2 tbsp
Lime 1, juice only
Rapeseed oil 2 tsp
Sweetcorn 165g tin, drained
Tomatoes 2, roughly chopped
Red chilli 1, deseeded and diced (optional)
Spring onions 2, finely chopped
Chopped fresh flat-leaf parsley 1-2 tbsp
Warmed tortilla wraps, sliced avocado, fresh coriander leaves, soured cream, grated cheese and lime wedges to serve

1 Put beef in a bowl and add peppers, onion, garlic, fajita seasoning, half the lime juice and oil; mix well.
2 Heat a large nonstick frying pan and cook beef and vegetable mixture for 3-4 minutes until cooked.
3 To prepare salsa, mix sweetcorn, tomatoes, chilli (if using), spring onions, remaining lime juice and parsley; set aside.
4 To assemble fajitas, spread some salsa on base of each tortilla, then add beef and vegetable mix. Serve with extra salsa, sliced avocado with fresh coriander, soured cream, grated cheese and lime wedges.

Serves 4 • Time 20 mins
Calories 282 • Fibre 4.3g • Salt 0.5g • Sugar 0.6g
Fat 11.4g of which 2.5g is saturated

67

14 Monday
St Valentine's Day

15 Tuesday

16 Wednesday
○ Full moon

17 Thursday

18 Friday

REMINDERS

Saturday 19

Sunday 20

RASPBERRY LOAF CAKE

Self-raising flour 200g (7oz)
Caster sugar 110g (4oz)
Butter 110g (4oz), softened
Medium eggs 2
Raspberry flavouring 1¼ tsp
Pink food colouring enough to colour cake, plus a
drop for icing (optional)
Raspberries 110g (4oz)
Icing sugar 75g (3oz)
Edible fruity confetti or hundreds and thousands
to decorate

1 Preheat oven to 190°C/170°fan/Gas 5. Grease and
line a 450g (1lb) loaf tin.
2 In a mixing bowl, mix together flour, caster sugar,
butter, eggs and 1 teaspoon raspberry flavouring.
3 If using, add just enough food colouring to make a
bright pink colour. Gently fold in raspberries.
4 Spoon mixture into tin and level top. Bake for
40-45 minutes or until a skewer comes out clean.
Cool on a wire rack.
5 Mix icing sugar with remaining raspberry flavouring,
a drop of pink food colouring (if using) and 1-2
tablespoons warm water. Drizzle over top of cake,
then sprinkle with edible fruity confetti or hundreds
and thousands.

TIPS Omit pink colouring for a natural-coloured cake
if preferred. The undecorated cake can be frozen.

Serves 8–10 • Time 1 hr plus cooling
Calories 300 • Fibre 1.5g • Salt 0.3g • Sugar 24g
Fat 12.8g of which 7.6g is saturated

21 Monday

22 Tuesday

23 Wednesday
(Last quarter

24 Thursday

25 Friday

REMINDERS

Sunday 27
Quinquagesima Sunday

CRACKLE TOP TIKKA PIE

Baby new potatoes 500g (1lb 2oz), peeled and thickly sliced
Vegetable oil 1 tbsp
Onion 1, peeled and finely sliced
Tikka curry paste 1 tbsp
Spinach 250g (9oz)
Fresh coriander 25g (1oz), roughly chopped
Chickpeas 400g tin, drained and rinsed
Plum tomatoes 400g tin, drained and roughly chopped
Unsweetened coconut yogurt 350g tub
Butter 25g (1oz), melted
Filo pastry 4 sheets, halved to make 8 squares

1 Preheat oven to 180°C/160°fan/Gas 4. Parboil potatoes in a pan of simmering water for 5 minutes, then drain.
2 Heat oil in a large frying pan. Add onion and fry for 5 minutes. Add tikka paste, cover and fry over a low-medium heat for 7-8 minutes, stirring occasionally, until softened.
3 Pile spinach into a colander over sink. Pour a kettle of boiling water over. Press water through using a spoon, working in batches if needed. Leave to drain.
4 Add coriander to pan, stir in chickpeas, tomatoes, potatoes, spinach and yogurt; season. Spoon into a 25cm (10in) pie dish.
5 Brush butter over filo and fold in concertina fashion to cover filling. Bake for 20 minutes until crisp and golden.
TIP Use remaining filo pastry to top another pie or to make tartlets.

Serves 4 • Time 1 hr
Calories 436 • Fibre 10.4g • Salt 0.9g • Sugar 1.9g
Fat 14.9g of which 4.8g is saturated

71

28 Monday

1 Tuesday MARCH
St David's Day
Shrove Tuesday

2 Wednesday
Ash Wednesday
● New moon

3 Thursday

4 Friday

REMINDERS

BLACK FOREST PANCAKES

Self-raising flour 50g (2oz)
Cocoa powder 15g (½oz)
Baking powder ½ tsp
Caster sugar 25g (1oz)
Dark chocolate chips 25g (1oz)
Sunflower oil 4 tsp
Medium egg 1, beaten
Semi-skimmed milk 4 tbsp
Kirsch 1 tbsp (optional)
Double cream 60ml (2fl oz), whipped
Ready-made cherry compote 100g (3½oz)

1 Sift flour, cocoa and baking powder into a bowl.
Stir in sugar and chocolate chips. Make a well in the
centre and gradually mix in 3 teaspoons of oil, and
egg and milk until well combined.
2 Heat a large frying pan over a low heat, then brush
lightly with a little of remaining oil. Use a tablespoon
measure to spoon 4 separate pools of mixture into
the pan. Cook for 2 minutes until bubbles appear and
the surface sets lightly.
3 Flip each pancake and cook for a further 2 minutes
until cooked through. Transfer to a plate, cover and
keep warm while cooking remaining batter to make
10 pancakes in total.
4 To serve, gently fold Kirsch, if using, into cream and
serve with pancakes and cherry compote.
TIP The cooked pancakes, without the toppings, are
suitable for freezing.

Makes 10 • Time 30 mins
Calories 334 • Fibre 2.4g • Salt 0g • Sugar 14.2g
Fat 21.7g of which 10.1g is saturated

7   Monday

8   Tuesday

9   Wednesday

10 Thursday
) First quarter

11 Friday

REMINDERS

Sunday 13

FAMILY TEATIME SNACK

Spinach 225g (8oz), rinsed
Cream cheese 250g tub
Chopped fresh tarragon 2 tbsp
Chopped fresh chives 2 tbsp
Chopped fresh parsley 4 tbsp
Spring onions 2, trimmed and finely sliced (optional)
Crumpets 8

1 Pile spinach into a large wide pan, cover and let leaves wilt over a medium heat for 2-3 minutes. Put into a colander over sink, drain water from leaves using a large spoon and roughly chop.
2 Soften cream cheese by stirring with a spoon and mix in all herbs and spring onions (if using). Season generously.
3 Toast crumpets until crisp and golden. Spread with herby cream cheese and spoon spinach on top. Serve warm.

Serves 4 • Time 10 mins
Calories 245 • Fibre 2.9g • Salt 2.1g • Sugar 0g
Fat 3.6g of which 1.6g is saturated

14 Monday
Commonwealth Day

15 Tuesday

16 Wednesday

17 Thursday
St Patrick's Day
Bank Holiday, Northern Ireland

18 Friday
○ Full moon

REMINDERS

STOUT & DATE LOAF

Butter 110g (4oz)
Dark brown muscovado sugar 75g (3oz)
Golden syrup 150g (5oz)
Guinness or other stout 150ml (5fl oz), plus 3 tbsp
Large eggs 2
Mixed spice 1 tsp
Ground ginger 2 tsp
Plain flour 225g (8oz)
Bicarbonate of soda 1 tsp
Dried pitted Deglet Nour dates 150g (5oz),
snipped into pieces with scissors
White chocolate 50g (2oz), finely chopped

1 Warm butter, sugar, syrup and 150ml (5fl oz) stout
in a large saucepan until butter melts. Stir well,
then leave for 10 minutes to cool. Preheat oven to
150°C/130°fan/Gas 2. Butter and line base of a 900g
(2lb) loaf tin.
2 Beat eggs into mixture in pan. Sift in spices, flour
and bicarbonate of soda; whisk to a smooth batter.
3 Stir in two-thirds of dates. Pour mixture into tin and
scatter rest of dates over top. Bake for 1 hour and 5
minutes until well risen and just firm to the touch.
4 Spoon rest of stout over cake and scatter chocolate
on top. Put cake back in oven for 5 minutes for
chocolate to melt. Spread softened chocolate over
cake as an icing. Cool in tin, then remove and cut into
thick slices.
TIP This cake keeps well. For an even more indulgent
twist, warm slices in the microwave and serve with a
dollop of crème fraîche.

Serves 12 • Time 1 hr 30 mins
Calories 270 • Fibre 1.5g • Salt 0.3g • Sugar 19g
Fat 10.1g of which 5.9g is saturated

21 Monday

22 Tuesday

23 Wednesday

24 Thursday

25 Friday
(Last quarter

REMINDERS

Saturday 26
Don't forget to put your clocks forward 1 hour tonight
(t.b.c. dependent on Government ruling)

Sunday 27
Mothering Sunday
Fourth Sunday in Lent

IRISH COFFEE ICE CREAM CHARLOTTE

Sponge fingers 20
Coffee-flavoured liqueur 6 tbsp
Vanilla ice cream 1 litre (1¾ pints)
Strong espresso coffee 4 tbsp
Maple syrup 6 tbsp
Chocolate-covered coffee beans 3 tbsp, chopped

1 Trim about 12 sponge fingers to fit base of a 20cm (8in) loose-bottomed sandwich tin lined with clingfilm or a reusable alternative. Dip biscuits in liqueur and fit into tin base. Halve rest of biscuits and use to line sides of tin, dipping in liqueur before you place them cut-side down around edge. Freeze for 15 minutes to firm up.
2 Meanwhile, remove ice cream from freezer to soften. Using a spoon, spread over sponge finger lining and freeze for at least 4 hours or until frozen.
3 Heat espresso and maple syrup in a small pan over a high heat. Bring to the boil and cook for a few minutes until syrupy. Cool. Remove pie from freezer 10 minutes before serving and transfer from tin onto a flat plate. Drizzle coffee syrup over and sprinkle with chopped coffee beans. Cut into wedges to serve.

TIPS Use Tia Maria or Kahlua for the liqueur. Decorate with grated chocolate, if you prefer.

Serves 8–10 • **Time 30 mins plus freezing**
Calories 249 • Fibre 0.5g • Salt 0.1g • Sugar 30.4g
Fat 7g of which 4.2g is saturated

79

28 Monday

29 Tuesday

30 Wednesday

31 Thursday

1 Friday APRIL
● New moon

REMINDERS

Sunday 3

LAMB & NOODLE BROTH

Rapeseed oil 1 tsp
Lean lamb leg steaks 4, trimmed and thinly sliced
Garlic cloves 2, peeled and finely chopped
Limes 2, finely grated zest and juice
Fresh root ginger 2.5cm (1in) piece, peeled and finely chopped
Ground turmeric ¼ tsp
Small red chilli 1, deseeded and finely sliced
Hot chicken stock 800ml (1¼ pints)
Soy sauce 2 tbsp
Red or yellow pepper 1, deseeded and finely sliced
Green beans 100g (3½oz), roughly chopped
Straight-to-wok rice noodles 150g (5oz)
Spring onions 2, finely chopped
Clear honey 2 tbsp
Chopped fresh coriander 2 tbsp

1 Heat oil in a large wok or saucepan until hot. Add lamb, garlic, lime zest, ginger, turmeric and chilli. Stir-fry for 1-2 minutes.
2 Add stock and soy sauce and cook for a further minute.
3 Add peppers and beans. Cook for a further 2-3 minutes. Add noodles, spring onions, honey and lime juice.
4 Spoon broth into 4 bowls and garnish with chopped coriander.

TIP If you prefer, add a few dried chilli flakes or substitute the lime zest with finely chopped lemongrass.

Serves 4 • Time 15 mins
Calories 312 • Fibre 2.9g • Salt 2.4g • Sugar 9.3g
Fat 12.5g of which 4.4g is saturated

4   Monday

5   Tuesday

6   Wednesday

7   Thursday

8   Friday

REMINDERS

CORONATION CAULIFLOWER & POTATO SALAD

Baby potatoes 250g (9oz), skins on and scrubbed
Small cauliflower florets 200g (7oz)
Onion 1, peeled and chopped
Olive oil 1 tbsp
Madras curry paste 1½ tsp
Reduced-fat mayonnaise 2 tbsp
Coconut milk yogurt 2 tbsp
Chunky mango chutney 3 tbsp
Prepared fresh mango 100g (3½oz), chopped
Salted cashews 25g (1oz), crushed
Fresh coriander a few sprigs (optional)

1 Preheat oven to 200°C/180°fan/Gas 6. Line a baking tray with baking paper. Halve or quarter potatoes if large. Mix in cauliflower, onion and oil.
2 Spread vegetables over baking tray in a single layer; season. Bake for 25 minutes, turning occasionally, until tender. Leave to cool, then drain, cover and chill until required.
3 To serve, mix curry paste, mayonnaise, yogurt and chutney together and carefully stir into vegetables. Pile into a serving bowl and top with mango, cashew nuts and coriander, if you like.
TIP For an alternative flavour twist, replace the curry paste and mango chutney with red or green pesto and tomato chutney and use a plain natural yogurt. Omit the mango and cashews and serve with chopped sundried tomatoes, olives, toasted pine nuts and fresh basil.

Serves 2 • **Time 40 mins plus cooling**
Calories 472 • Fibre 9.6g • Salt 1.9g • Sugar 13.7g
Fat 23.1g of which 2.8g is saturated

83

11 Monday

12 Tuesday

13 Wednesday

14 Thursday

15 Friday
Good Friday
Bank Holiday, UK

REMINDERS

Saturday 16
○ Full moon

Sunday 17
Easter Day

MILLIONAIRE'S EASTER CHOCOLATE BARS

Butter 190g (6½oz)
Shortbread fingers 250g (9oz), finely crushed
White chocolate 200g (7oz)
Tinned caramel 200g (7oz)
Caramel flavouring (optional)
Dark chocolate 110g (4oz)
Milk chocolate 110g (4oz)
Mini eggs 100g (3½oz), lightly crushed

1 Line a 20cm (8in) square tin with a double layer of foil so that it hangs over the sides of the tin. Melt 75g (3oz) butter. Tip crushed shortbread into a bowl and mix in melted butter. Cool for 10 minutes, then press evenly over the base of the tin. Chill for 30 minutes.
2 Break white chocolate into a heatproof bowl and melt over a saucepan of barely simmering water. Remove from water and stir in caramel and flavouring to taste, if using. Spread over shortbread base. Leave to cool, then chill for 30 minutes to firm up.
3 Break dark and milk chocolate into a saucepan. Add remaining butter along with 3 tablespoons water. Heat gently, stirring, until melted together. Remove from the heat, stir well and leave to cool for 15 minutes, then spoon on top of caramel filling and smooth top. Scatter with the crushed eggs; leave to cool completely, then chill for at least 1 hour to set.
4 To serve, carefully remove from the tin using the foil to help you and place on a board. Cut into 12-15 bars. Keep chilled.

Makes 12–15 • Time 30 mins plus cooling and chilling
Calories 420 • Fibre 0.9g • Salt 0.3g • Sugar 31.2g
Fat 28.5g of which 17.5g is saturated

18 Monday
Easter Monday
Bank Holiday, England, Wales and Northern Ireland

19 Tuesday

20 Wednesday

21 Thursday

22 Friday

REMINDERS

TEAR & SHARE EASTER BUNS

White bread mix 500g pack
Unwaxed lemons 2, finely grated zest and juice
Caster sugar 50g (2oz)
Ground cinnamon 1½ tsp
Olive oil 2 tbsp
Medium egg 1, beaten
Ready-rolled white icing 225g (8oz), chopped
Vanilla extract 1 tsp
Sugar flowers to decorate

1 Line a large baking tray with baking paper and draw an 18cm (7in) circle in the centre. Put bread mix in a bowl and mix in lemon zest, sugar and cinnamon. Make a well in centre.
2 Put oil and lemon juice in a jug and make up to the recommended liquid level with water as directed. Mix, rest and knead according to the packet instructions.
3 Divide dough into 16 equal portions and shape each into a neat ball. Arrange 8 evenly spaced on the outside edge of the drawn circle to create a ring. Arrange remaining 8 buns inside the circle to make a second ring. Cover with a piece of oiled clingfilm or a reusable alternative and leave to rise as directed.
4 Preheat oven to 220°C/200°fan/Gas 7. Brush tops of buns with egg and bake for 20 minutes or until deeply golden. Transfer to a wire rack to cool completely.
5 Put icing in a small pan with vanilla and 4 teaspoons water. Heat gently until very soft and melted. Mix well, spoon thickly over each bun and decorate with flowers. Leave to set briefly before serving.
TIP The uniced buns are suitable for freezing.

Makes 16 • **Time 1 hr plus proving**
Calories 185 • Fibre 0.8g • Salt 0.3g • Sugar 16.3g
Fat 2.2g of which 0.4g is saturated

87

25 Monday

26 Tuesday

27 Wednesday

28 Thursday

29 Friday

REMINDERS

Saturday 30
● New moon

MAY Sunday 1

CELERIAC SOUP WITH CHEESE & WALNUTS

Butter 25g (1oz)
Celeriac 1 large, peeled and chopped
Leek 1, trimmed and sliced
Large potato 1, peeled and chopped
English dessert apples 2, peeled, cored and roughly chopped
Vegetable stock 1.25 litres (2 pints)
Cheddar cheese 50g (2oz), grated
Walnuts 25g (1oz), toasted
Chunky bread, sliced, to serve (optional)

1 Melt butter in a large pan. Add celeriac, leek, potato, apples and pinch of salt. Cook gently for 10 minutes, stirring occasionally, until starting to soften.
2 Pour in stock, bring to boil, then simmer for 20 minutes.
3 Use a stick blender or jug blender to whizz mixture until partially smooth or completely smooth, depending on your preference. Season to taste and add boiling water if consistency is too thick.
4 Ladle into warm bowls and scatter with cheese and walnuts. Serve with chunky slices of bread, if you like.
TIP Any leftovers will keep in the fridge for a few days or can be frozen.

Serves 5–6 • Time 45 mins
Calories 164 • Fibre 3.9g • Salt 1.4g • Sugar 0g
Fat 10g of which 4.6g is saturated

2 Monday
Bank Holiday, UK

3 Tuesday

4 Wednesday

5 Thursday

6 Friday

REMINDERS

Saturday 7

Sunday 8

DOLCELATTE & OLIVE TAGLIATELLE

Tagliatelle 150g (5oz)
Walnut pieces 25g (1oz)
Fresh parsley 25g (1oz), thick stalks removed
Fresh mint leaves a handful
Garlic 1 clove, peeled and roughly chopped
Stale bread 1 small slice
Lemon ½, finely grated zest and juice
Olive oil 6 tbsp
Dolcelatte cheese 50g (2oz), crumbled
Pitted black olives 10-12, halved

1 Cook pasta in boiling water for 8–10 minutes until just tender.
2 Meanwhile, toast walnuts in a small pan.
Put parsley, mint leaves and garlic in a large jug, tear in the bread, add lemon zest and juice, and oil. Using a stick blender, whizz to a rough paste and season to taste. Add toasted walnuts and whizz again to incorporate but retain the rough texture.
3 Drain pasta, keeping back some water. Return pasta to pan, stir in half the sauce and 2-3 tablespoons cooking water. Divide pasta between two warmed bowls; dot with cheese and olives. Serve immediately.
TIPS This recipe makes enough sauce to serve 4. The rest of the sauce will keep in a jar in the fridge for a week. Double the pasta portion if serving 4. Serve any remaining sauce with chicken or chops or on top of fried flat mushrooms.

Serves 2 • Time 15 mins
Calories 465 • Fibre 6.2g • Salt 1.5g • Sugar 0.3g
Fat 17g of which 6.6g is saturated

91

9 Monday
) First quarter

10 Tuesday

11 Wednesday

12 Thursday

13 Friday

REMINDERS

HARISSA SHOULDER OF LAMB

Whole shoulder of lamb 1.8kg (4lb)
Harissa paste 4 tbsp
Rapeseed oil 1 tbsp
Hot lamb or vegetable stock 200ml (7fl oz)
Greek-style natural yogurt 100ml (3½fl oz)
Chopped fresh mint 15g (½oz)
Fresh pomegranate seeds 100g tub
Lemon ½, juice only
Cooked rice or couscous to serve

1 Preheat oven to 160°C/140°fan/Gas 3.
2 Place lamb on a chopping board and make
several slashes over surface of lamb with a
sharp knife. Season and spread with harissa
paste and oil on both sides. Transfer to a
large nonstick roasting tin. Pour over stock.
3 Cover with baking paper then foil and
roast for 4 hours. Remove joint from tin,
transfer to a chopping board and 'pull'
cooked lamb apart by securing with a fork
and shredding meat with a second fork.
4 Drizzle with yogurt, then garnish with
mint, pomegranate seeds and lemon juice.
Serve with prepared rice or couscous.

Serves 6 • Time 4 hrs 15 mins
Calories 669 • Fibre 0.1g • Salt 0.9g • Sugar 0g
Fat 48.8g of which 22.5g is saturated

93

16 Monday
○ Full moon

17 Tuesday

18 Wednesday

19 Thursday

20 Friday

REMINDERS

Saturday 21

Sunday 22
Rogation Sunday
☾ Last quarter

SPRING SUNSHINE CHICKEN

Lemons 2, finely grated zest and juice of 1, the other cut into 8 wedges
Saffron threads a good pinch
Garlic 1-2 cloves, peeled and grated
Greek yogurt 4 tbsp
Chicken legs 4, trimmed of excess skin and fat
New potatoes 500g (1lb 2oz), washed
Large onion 1, peeled and sliced
Olive oil 2 tbsp
Fresh parsley a good bunch
Pistachio kernels 2 tbsp, roughly chopped
Spring greens, green beans or peas to serve

1 Put lemon zest and juice in a large dish, add saffron mixed with 1 tablespoon hot water and garlic. Stir in yogurt and a pinch of salt. Add chicken legs and coat well. Cover and chill for at least 2 hours or overnight.
2 Preheat oven to 190°C/170°fan/Gas 5. Parboil potatoes for 5 minutes, drain and cut in half if large. Put into a large roasting tin along with onion. Mix in oil, season, then place chicken on top, spooning over excess marinade. Roast for 35 minutes.
3 Tuck lemon wedges in between chicken pieces and cook for another 25-35 minutes until chicken is well-cooked and juices run clear. Sprinkle with torn parsley leaves and pistachios. Serve with green vegetables of your choice
TIP While the oven heats up, you could roast the whole pistachios on a baking tray for 5 minutes, then chop and set aside.

Serves 4 • **Time 1 hr 15 mins plus chilling**
Calories 607 • Fibre 4.3g • Salt 1.1g • Sugar 0g
Fat 38.9g of which 10.9g is saturated

23 Monday

24 Tuesday

25 Wednesday

26 Thursday
Ascension Day
Holy Thursday

27 Friday

REMINDERS

Saturday 28

Sunday 29

RAINBOW STUFFED PEPPERS

Small red, green and yellow peppers 1 of each
Pork sausages 125g (4½oz)
Olive oil 2 tbsp
Cooking chorizo 75g (3oz), skinned and chopped
Spring onions 2, trimmed and chopped
Tomatoes 2, chopped
Sweet smoked paprika 2 tsp
Ready-cooked mixed grains 125g (4½ oz)
Green leafy salad to serve

1 Preheat the oven to 190°C/170°fan/Gas 5. Halve peppers lengthways through stalk. Scoop out seeds and white membrane, leaving pepper skins intact. Arrange sausages and peppers (cut-side up) snugly in a baking dish. Brush with half the oil, season, cover with foil and bake for 35 minutes.
2 Mix together remaining ingredients except coriander, season to taste and set aside.
3 After 35 minutes, remove peppers from oven and carefully drain cooking juices into grain mixture. Chop sausages and stir into grains, then pile into peppers. Re-cover with foil.
4 Bake for a further 30 minutes, removing foil for final 10 minutes of cooking until tender and lightly browned. Serve immediately with green leafy salad.
TIPS For a veggie version, replace the meat with diced halloumi or Feta cheese. For a vegan version, try vegan sausage or smoked tofu.

Serves 2–3 • **Time 1 hr 10 mins**
Calories 395 • Fibre 5.1g • Salt 1.8g • Sugar 0g
Fat 27.9g of which 8.3g is saturated

97

30 Monday
● New moon

31 Tuesday

1 Wednesday JUNE

2 Thursday
Coronation Day
Elizabeth II's 70th Anniversary celebrations
Bank Holiday, UK

3 Friday
Elizabeth II's 70th Anniversary celebrations
Bank Holiday, UK

REMINDERS

ITALIAN-STYLE COTTAGE PIE

Olive oil 2 tbsp
Small onion 1, peeled and finely chopped
Garlic 1 clove, peeled and crushed
Carrot 1, peeled and finely chopped
Celery stick 1, finely chopped
Chestnut mushrooms 125g (4½oz), chopped
Lean minced beef 250g (9oz)
Red wine 100ml (3½fl oz)
Tinned chopped tomatoes 200g (7oz)
Dried oregano 1 tsp
Gnocchi 350g (12oz)
Grated mozzarella 50g (2oz)
Grated Parmesan 2 tbsp
Fresh basil and salad leaves to serve (optional)

1 Heat 1 tbsp oil in a large saucepan and gently fry onion, garlic, carrot and celery for 10 minutes until softened. Add mushrooms and beef and continue to cook, stirring, for 3-4 minutes until browned all over.
2 Add wine, tomatoes and oregano; season. Bring to the boil, partially cover and simmer gently for 30 minutes until tender. Transfer to an ovenproof baking dish and leave to cool.
3 Cook gnocchi according to the packet instructions. Drain, rinse in cold water and leave to cool.
4 To cook, preheat oven to 190°C/170°fan/Gas 5. Heat remaining oil in a large frying pan, then stir fry gnocchi for about 5 minutes until lightly browned. Drain and spoon on top of meat mixture. Sprinkle cheeses over. Bake for 35 minutes until golden. Tear over fresh basil and accompany with salad leaves to serve, if you like.

Serves 2–3 • Time 1 hr 30 mins plus cooling
Calories 493 • Fibre 5.5g • Salt 1.6g • Sugar 1.3g
Fat 18.6g of which 7.7g is saturated

99

6   Monday

7   Tuesday
) First quarter

8   Wednesday

9   Thursday

10 Friday

REMINDERS

Saturday 11

Sunday 12
Trinity Sunday

BRITISH ASPARAGUS SALAD WITH SPICED OATS

Egg 1, white only
Soy sauce 1 tbsp
Jumbo oats 100g (3½oz)
Sesame seeds 2 tbsp
British asparagus 2 bunches, trimmed
Olive oil 2 tbsp
Greek yogurt 3 tbsp
Tahini 2 tbsp
Lemon ½, juice only
Babyleaf spinach 2 large handfuls
Avocados 2 ripe, peeled and chopped

1 Preheat oven to 200°C/180°fan/Gas 6. To make spiced oats, add egg white and soy sauce to a mixing bowl and whisk for 1-2 minutes until pale and foamy. Add oats, sesame seeds and seasoning and mix until well combined.
2 Tip onto a nonstick baking tray, spreading out into a thin layer. Bake in oven for 12-15 minutes, stirring halfway through, until crisp and golden-brown.
3 Meanwhile, place asparagus on another baking tray and drizzle over olive oil. Season and roast for 6-8 minutes until just tender.
4 Put yogurt, tahini and lemon juice in a bowl and whisk together with enough cold water to get a drizzling consistency. Season and set aside.
5 Scatter spinach over a large serving plate. Scatter avocado over spinach. Top the salad with asparagus and drizzle dressing over. Scatter over crunchy oats and serve warm.

Serves 4 • Time 30 mins
Calories 521 • Fibre 9.5g • Salt 0.6g • Sugar 0g
Fat 41.7g of which 8.7g is saturated

101

13 Monday

14 Tuesday
○ Full moon

15 Wednesday

16 Thursday
Corpus Christi

17 Friday

REMINDERS

COD & PRAWN BURGERS WITH HERB MAYONNAISE

Skinless cod fillet 500g (1lb 2oz)
Raw prawns 100g (3½oz)
Garlic 2 cloves, peeled and crushed
Capers 2 tbsp, chopped
Chopped fresh dill 1 tsp
English mustard 1 tsp
Rapeseed oil 1 tbsp
Chopped fresh tarragon 1 tbsp, chopped
Chopped flat-leaf parsley 2 tbsp
Mayonnaise 50g (2oz)
Wholegrain mustard 1 tsp
Burger buns, lettuce leaves, sliced tomato, sliced red onion and lemon wedges to serve

1 Place cod and prawns on a plate; season. Cover and chill for 1 hour, then finely chop.
2 In a bowl, mix together cod, prawns, garlic, capers, dill and English mustard. Put mixture into a food processor and blend until combined. Shape into 4 burgers, cover with clingfilm or a reusable alternative and rest in the fridge for 1 hour.
3 Heat oil in a large frying pan over a medium heat. Remove burgers from fridge and gently fry for 4-6 minutes, turning a few times, until cooked through. Alternatively, deep-fry, if you prefer.
4 Meanwhile, mix tarragon, parsley and mayonnaise in a bowl. Stir in wholegrain mustard.
5 Toast buns and layer lettuce, tomato and onion with mayo. Add burgers and serve with lemon wedges.

Serves 4 • Time 15 mins plus chilling and resting
Calories 666 • Fibre 2.9g • Salt 1.6g • Sugar 0g
Fat 43.6g of which 3.9g is saturated

20 Monday

21 Tuesday
(Last quarter
Summer solstice
Summer begins

22 Wednesday

23 Thursday

24 Friday

REMINDERS

Saturday 25

Sunday 26

ENGLISH HEDGEROW SPRITZER

Elderflower cordial 100ml (3½fl oz)
Dry white wine 400ml (12½fl oz)
Sparkling water 300ml (½ pint)
Fresh mint 4 sprigs
Ice cubes to serve

1 Pour cordial, wine and sparkling water into a jug and stir well.
2 Add a mint sprig and a few ice cubes to 4 large wine or gin glasses. Fill glasses with spritzer to serve.

Serves 4 • Time 5 mins
Calories 142 • Fibre 0g • Salt 0g • Sugar 13.2g
Fat 0g of which 0g is saturated

105

27 Monday

28 Tuesday

29 Wednesday
● New moon

30 Thursday

1 Friday JULY

REMINDERS

Saturday 2

Sunday 3

BANANA TARTINE

Fruit bread 4 thick slices
Ricotta cheese 110g (4oz)
Bananas 2 small, sliced
Chopped pistachios 1 tbsp
Clear honey 4 tsp
Strawberries a handful, sliced
(optional)

1 Toast fruit bread slices, then spread
with ricotta and arrange slices of
banana on top.
2 Sprinkle with chopped pistachios
and drizzle with honey. Serve with
sliced strawberries, if you like.
TIPS Use sourdough or brioche
instead of fruit bread if you prefer.
Any chopped nuts will work well in
this recipe: try pecans or hazelnuts.

Serves 4 • Time 5 mins
Calories 221 • Fibre 2.1g • Salt 0.3g • Sugar 9g
Fat 5.9g of which 2.4g is saturated

4   Monday

5   Tuesday

6   Wednesday

7   Thursday
) First quarter

8   Friday

REMINDERS

Saturday 9

Sunday 10

SEARED SALMON WITH WATERMELON & MINT SALSA

Wild Alaska salmon 4 x 125g (4½oz) fillets
Fennel seeds 2 tbsp
Olive oil 2 tbsp
Watermelon 1 wedge, deseeded and finely chopped
Lime 1, finely grated zest and juice
Small red onion 1, peeled and finely chopped
Mint leaves a few, roughly chopped
Caster sugar a pinch
Salad leaves to serve

1 Sprinkle each salmon fillet with a few fennel seeds.
2 Heat oil in a frying pan and add salmon fillets, skin-side down. Cook over a high heat for 2-3 minutes to crisp the skin, then turn heat down and turn fillets over. Cook for another 2-3 minutes, then turn off heat.
3 Make salsa by combining watermelon, lime zest and juice, red onion and mint leaves. Season with a pinch of sugar, salt and black pepper.
4 Serve salmon with salad leaves, and salsa spooned on top.

Serves 4 • Time 10 mins
Calories 305 • Fibre 0.7g • Salt 0.7g • Sugar 1g
Fat 19.8g of which 3.5g is saturated

11 Monday

12 Tuesday
Bank Holiday, Northern Ireland

13 Wednesday
○ Full moon

14 Thursday

15 Friday

REMINDERS

Saturday 16

Sunday 17

CUCUMBER PICKLE

Cucumber 250g (9oz)
Small red onion 1, peeled and finely chopped
Fresh dill a few sprigs
Cider vinegar 250ml (9fl oz)
Granulated sugar 125g (4½oz)
Bay leaf 1
Mustard seeds 1 tsp, finely crushed
Coriander seeds 1 tsp, finely crushed

1 Cut cucumber into 1cm (½in) thick pieces.
Place in a bowl. Mix onion into cucumber with
1 tablespoon of salt. Cover and leave to stand
at room temperature for 1 hour.
2 Drain vegetables in a large sieve and rinse
very well in cold running water. Dry using
absorbent kitchen paper. Pack into sterilised
jam jars with a generous amount of dill,
making sure there is room at the top of jars for
liquid to level out and cover vegetables. Stand
jars on a board and cover loosely.
3 Pour vinegar into a saucepan and add
remaining ingredients. Heat gently, stirring,
until sugar dissolves, then increase heat and
boil for 3 minutes. Discard bay leaf.
4 Pour hot spiced vinegar over vegetables,
making sure completely covered. Seal tightly
with a non-corrosive lid and leave to cool.
5 Label, date and store in a cool, dry cupboard
for at least 3 months before opening.

Makes 2 jars • Time 20 mins plus salting
Calories 18 • Fibre 0.2g • Salt 0.1g • Sugar 4.2g
Fat 0.1g of which 0g is saturated

111

18 Monday

19 Tuesday

20 Wednesday
(Last quarter

21 Thursday

22 Friday

REMINDERS

Saturday 23

Sunday 24

SUMMER BEAN, SAMPHIRE & TROUT SALAD

New potatoes 250-300g (9-11oz), scrubbed
Runner beans 150g (5oz), shredded with a bean slicer or cut into 4cm (1½in) lengths on the diagonal
Samphire 50g (2oz)
Trout fillets 250g (9oz)
Lemon ½, finely grated zest and 1-2 tbsp juice
Crème fraîche 3 heaped tbsp
Fresh chives 10 stalks
Little Gem lettuce 1 small, leaves separated
Mint leaves 10-12, shredded

1 Cook potatoes in a pan of simmering water for 20 minutes or until tender. After about 10 minutes, put beans and samphire in a steamer above the potatoes and cook for 5–6 minutes until just softening. Cool beans and samphire under cold running water and leave to drain well. Put trout on a piece of baking paper in the steamer and steam for 4-6 minutes until just cooked. Remove skin from fish.
2 Whisk together lemon zest, juice and crème fraîche in a serving bowl. Snip in chives and season well. Add lettuce leaves and drained potatoes, beans and samphire and mix lightly to coat in the dressing.
3 Arrange large flakes of trout on top of salad. Sprinkle with shredded mint leaves.

TIPS If you can't get hold of samphire, use fine asparagus tips. Use salmon or mackerel instead of trout, if preferred.

Serves 2 • Time 25 mins
Calories 419 • Fibre 4.8g • Salt 1.9g • Sugar 0g
Fat 23.1g of which 12.5g is saturated

25 Monday

26 Tuesday

27 Wednesday

28 Thursday

● New moon

29 Friday

REMINDERS

Saturday 30

Sunday 31

TROPICAL FLOURLESS CHOCOLATE TRUFFLE CAKE

Coconut oil 250g (9oz), plus extra for greasing
Dark chocolate 250g (9oz)
Large eggs 6, separated
Caster sugar 250g (9oz)
Cocoa powder 75g (3oz)
Prepared fresh mango, pineapple and banana 350g (12oz)
Lime 1, finely grated zest and juice
Coconut milk yogurt 250g (9oz)

1 Preheat oven to 180°C/160°fan/Gas 4. Grease and line a 23cm (9in) springform cake tin. Put oil in a saucepan and break chocolate into pieces on top. Melt over a very low heat until combined, then mix well and cool for 10 minutes.
2 Whisk egg yolks and sugar together in a large bowl for 2-3 minutes until thick, creamy and pale. Gently stir in melted chocolate mixture.
3 In another bowl, whisk egg whites until stiff. Add a large spoonful to chocolate and gently stir in.
4 Sift cocoa powder on top and carefully fold in remaining egg white until well combined. Spoon into tin, smooth top and stand tin on a baking tray. Bake for 40-45 minutes until slightly risen and cracked. Put tin on a wire rack and leave cake to cool (it will sink).
5 To serve, gently mix prepared fruit with lime juice and most of the zest. Pile coconut yogurt into centre of cake and spoon fruit on top. Sprinkle remaining zest over.

TIP The undecorated cake can be frozen.

Serves 10–12 • Time 1 hr 30 mins plus cooling
Calories 464 • Fibre 2.5g • Salt 0.2g • Sugar 34.8g
Fat 31.4g of which 23.3g is saturated

115

1 Monday
Bank Holiday, Scotland

2 Tuesday

3 Wednesday

4 Thursday

5 Friday
) First quarter

REMINDERS

Saturday 6

Sunday 7

SALMON SATAY SKEWERS

Wild Alaska salmon 4 x 125g (4½oz) fillets
Crunchy peanut butter 70g (2¾oz)
Light soy sauce 2 tbsp
Sweet chilli sauce 3 tbsp
Lime 1, 2 tbsp juice, rest cut into wedges
Red pepper 1, deseeded and cut into chunks
Yellow pepper 1, deseeded and cut into chunks
Courgettes 2, sliced
Olive oil for brushing
Carrots 2, peeled and pared into ribbons
Lettuce leaves a few, shredded
Beansprouts 100g (3½oz)
Sesame seeds 2 tsp, toasted

1 Remove and discard skin from salmon and cut into large chunks. Put into a shallow, non-metallic dish.
2 Mix peanut butter, soy, chilli sauce and lime juice. Add half to salmon, tossing to coat, then cover and leave to marinate for at least 20 minutes.
3 Preheat barbecue or grill. Thread salmon onto 4 large or 8 small skewers with peppers and courgettes. Arrange on preheated barbecue or grill rack, brush with oil and cook for 5-6 minutes, turning occasionally, until cooked through.
4 Meanwhile, mix carrot ribbons with lettuce and beansprouts. Add 1-2 tbsp water to remaining satay sauce to make a dressing.
5 Serve salmon skewers with salad, drizzled with dressing and sprinkled with sesame seeds and black pepper. Garnish with lime wedges.

Serves 4 • Time 30 mins
Calories 465 • Fibre 5.4g • Salt 1.9g • Sugar 8g
Fat 29.5g of which 5.5g is saturated

117

8 Monday

---

9 Tuesday

---

10 Wednesday

---

11 Thursday

---

12 Friday
○ Full moon

REMINDERS

CRAYFISH COCKTAIL CROÛTES

Ciabatta loaf ½, cut into 8 slices on the diagonal
Olive oil 2 tbsp
Mayonnaise 3 tbsp
Tomato ketchup ½ tbsp
Worcestershire sauce ½ tsp
Lemon 1, cut into 6 wedges
Crayfish tails 120g pack
Avocado 1 ripe, halved and stone removed
Little Gem lettuce 8 leaves
Smoked paprika or cayenne pepper to serve

1 Preheat the grill or a griddle pan. Brush ciabatta with most of the oil and toast on both sides until slightly browned.
2 Mix mayonnaise, ketchup and Worcestershire sauce in a bowl and add juice from one lemon wedge. Stir in crayfish and season well.
3 Scoop avocado flesh into a bowl and mash with remaining oil and juice from another lemon wedge. Spread thickly onto toasted ciabatta. Put a lettuce leaf on top. Spoon crayfish mixture into lettuce leaf. Sprinkle with a little paprika or cayenne and garnish with lemon wedges.

TIPS You can use prawns instead of crayfish, and crème fraîche instead of mayonnaise. Add chilli sauce instead of ketchup for a bit of a kick to the sauce. Sprinkle with snipped chives instead of paprika or cayenne.

Serves 2 • Time 15 mins
Calories 610 kcal • Fibre 5.5g • Salt 1.1g • Sugar 3.6g
Fat 40.6g of which 5.4g is saturated

15 Monday

16 Tuesday

17 Wednesday

18 Thursday

19 Friday
(Last quarter

REMINDERS

Saturday 20

Sunday 21

STRAWBERRY CARDAMOM COMPOTE

Green cardamom pods 5
Orange blossom honey 2 tbsp, plus extra to serve
Vanilla bean paste 1 tsp
Lime 1, pared zest and 2 tbsp juice
Strawberries 300g (11oz), hulled and quartered if large
Natural yogurt 4 heaped tbsp
Pistachios 2 tbsp, roughly chopped

1 Put cardamom pods in a small pan. Bash lightly with the end of a rolling pin, then add honey, vanilla, zest and juice to pan with strawberries. Simmer over a low-medium heat for 8-10 minutes, stirring occasionally until fruit is just soft but holds its shape.
2 Remove and discard cardamom pods and pared zest. Serve warm or cold with a generous dollop of yogurt per portion, sprinkled with pistachios and drizzled with extra honey.

Serves 4 • Time 15 mins
Calories 143 • Fibre 3.6g • Salt 0.2g • Sugar 9.2g
Fat 6.4g of which 1.1g is saturated

121

22 Monday

23 Tuesday

24 Wednesday

25 Thursday

26 Friday

REMINDERS

Saturday 27

● New moon

Sunday 28

BRAZILIAN PRAWN STEW

Olive oil 1 tbsp
Celery 3 sticks, finely sliced
Green pepper 1, deseeded and finely chopped
Garlic cloves 3, peeled and chopped
Green chilli 1, deseeded and sliced
Cayenne pepper ½ tsp
Large tomatoes 2, skinned & chopped
Spring onions 6, cut into 2cm (¾in) chunks
Coconut milk 400ml (14fl oz)
Vegetable stock 150ml (¼ pint)
Raw king prawns 150g (5oz)
Fresh coriander small bunch
Lemon 1, cut into wedges
Cooked rice or chunky bread to serve

1 In a large saucepan, heat oil over a medium heat and gently cook celery and pepper for 4-5 minutes with the lid on, stirring occasionally, until they start to soften.
2 Add garlic, chilli and cayenne and stir. After 1 minute stir in tomatoes and spring onions. Cook for 3-4 minutes, then add coconut milk and stock. Bring to the boil.
3 Add prawns and season. Simmer gently for 5-6 minutes until prawns are cooked. Adjust seasoning to taste, then divide stew between bowls. Top with coriander and lemon wedges. Serve with rice or a hunk of bread.

Serves 2 • Time 30 mins
Calories 213 • Fibre 4.6g • Salt 1.5g • Sugar 0g
Fat 7.6g of which 1.5g is saturated

29 Monday
Bank Holiday, England, Wales and Northern Ireland

30 Tuesday

31 Wednesday

1 Thursday SEPTEMBER

2 Friday

REMINDERS

SOFT-BAKE CARROT CAKE COOKIES

Plain flour 225g (8oz)
Baking powder 1 tsp
Ground cinnamon 1½ tsp
Pecan nuts 25g (1oz), finely chopped
Sultanas 75g (3oz)
Grated carrot 150g (5oz)
Medium egg 1, beaten
Sunflower oil 6 tbsp
Clear honey 75g (3oz)
Unsalted butter 65g (2½oz), very soft
Soft cheese 125g (4½oz)
Icing sugar 65g (2½oz)
Vanilla extract 1 tsp

1 Preheat oven to 180°C/160°fan/Gas 4. Line
2 baking trays with baking paper. Sift flour, baking
powder and cinnamon into a bowl and stir in pecans,
sultanas and 100g (3½oz) grated carrot. Make a well
in the centre.
2 Add egg, oil and honey and mix well to make a
soft dough. Drop heaped teaspoonfuls, spaced apart
to allow for spreading, onto trays and flatten tops
slightly with the back of a wet spoon.
3 Bake for 20 minutes until firm and lightly golden.
Leave to cool on trays, then transfer to an airtight
container. Like this, they will store for up to 5 days.
4 To serve, mix butter and soft cheese until combined.
Sift icing sugar over, add vanilla and mix well. Spoon
on top of each cookie. Sprinkle with remaining carrot.
TIP The cookies (without icing) can be frozen.

Makes 24 • Time 40 mins plus cooling
Calories 132 • Fibre 3.3g • Salt 0.6g • Sugar 0g
Fat 7.3g of which 2.7g is saturated

125

5   Monday

6   Tuesday

7   Wednesday

8   Thursday

9   Friday

REMINDERS

Saturday 10
○ Full moon

Sunday 11

QUICK-COOKED RADISHES & KALE

Olive oil 1 tbsp
Garlic 2 cloves, peeled and sliced
Radishes 200g (7oz), halved
Chopped kale 250g (9oz)
Fresh thyme generous handful of sprigs, leaves stripped from the stalks

1 Heat olive oil in a large frying pan and add garlic, radishes, kale and thyme. Toss in pan for 5-7 minutes until kale is crispy at the edges and radishes have softened slightly. Season to taste.
TIP French Breakfast radishes work well here. Serve with white fish or lamb, if you like.

Serves 4 • **Time 15 mins**
Calories 54 • Fibre 3.3g • Salt 0.6g • Sugar 0g
Fat 3.9g of which 0.6g is saturated

12 Monday

13 Tuesday

14 Wednesday

15 Thursday

16 Friday

REMINDERS

Saturday 17
(Last quarter

Sunday 18

SMOKED MACKEREL WITH BEETROOT ON RYE

Crème fraîche 4 tbsp
Hot horseradish sauce 1 tbsp
Lemon ½, finely grated zest and some juice
Smoked mackerel fillets 2, skinned
Olive oil 1 tbsp
Rye sourdough bread 3 slices
Cooked beetroot 2, thinly sliced
Fresh dill or parsley a few sprigs
Rocket and baby red chard leaves to serve
(optional)

1 Mix crème fraîche, horseradish sauce, lemon zest and a little juice in a bowl.
2 Break fish into large flakes into sauce and season to taste.
3 Preheat grill to high or heat a griddle pan over a high heat. Brush oil over bread and toast for about 1 minute on each side.
4 Arrange slices of beetroot on toast. Spoon fish mixture over beetroot and sprinkle with dill or parsley and freshly ground black pepper. Cut each toast in half and serve with rocket and baby red chard leaves, if you like.
TIP If you can get fresh horseradish, grate in ½-1 tablespoon for a really fresh kick.

Serves 2 • Time 10 mins
Calories 495 • Fibre 3.3g • Salt 2.2g • Sugar 0g
Fat 36.5g of which 12.6g is saturated

19 Monday

20 Tuesday

21 Wednesday

22 Thursday

23 Friday
Autumnal equinox
Autumn begins

REMINDERS

Sunday 25
● New moon

WIN A PORTMEIRION BOTANIC GARDEN
HARMONY SET WORTH £258!

Striking butterfly motifs take centre stage across this award-winning collection from Portmeirion.

With a modern take on retro design, coloured glazes wash over plates and bowls. Embossed textures accentuate pieces to make for a wonderfully tactile and intriguing range.

Made in Portmeirion's factory in Stoke-on-Trent, England, you can be sure of the best levels of quality.

Enter at **dairydiary.co.uk/win2022**
Or send in your name and address to:
Dairy Diary 2022 Prize Draw,
Barn 3, Somerford Business Court
Holmes Chapel Road, Somerford
Congleton, CW12 4SN
Closing date 30 November 2022

You can order your 2023 Dairy Diary via your milkman (see p170),
or direct from the publisher at dairydiary.co.uk or by phoning 0344 4725265.

26 Monday

27 Tuesday

28 Wednesday

29 Thursday

30 Friday

REMINDERS

Saturday 1

Sunday 2

ROAST PLUMS WITH RUM, GINGER & TREACLE CREAM

Red plums 12, halved and stoned
Stem ginger 2 pieces, finely sliced
Muscovado sugar 8 tbsp
Orange juice 4 tbsp
Dark rum 6 tbsp
Double cream 175ml (6fl oz)
Greek yogurt 175g (6oz)

1 Preheat oven to 180°C/160°fan/Gas 4.
Arrange plums, cut-side up, in a large
ovenproof dish so they sit snugly in one
layer, if possible. Scatter stem ginger and
half the sugar over. Pour in orange juice and
rum. Bake for 25-40 minutes (depending on
ripeness of plums) until fruit is tender but still
holds its shape. Leave to cool completely.
2 Whip double cream to very soft peaks, then
fold in yogurt. Spoon into a serving bowl and
sprinkle evenly with remaining sugar. Cover
with foil or baking paper and chill. The sugar
will dissolve and become soft and treacly.
Swirl into cream for serving with plums.
TIPS If you cannot remove the stones from
the plums before cooking, they can be
removed afterwards. Make the cream mixture
6-12 hours before you plan to serve it.

Serves 6 • **Time 45 mins plus chilling**
Calories 318 • Fibre 1.3g • Salt 0.1g • Sugar 25.6g
Fat 18.2g of which 11.4g is saturated

3   Monday
) First quarter

4   Tuesday

5   Wednesday

6   Thursday

7   Friday

REMINDERS

MISO & SESAME AUBERGINE

Aubergine 1, trimmed
Miso Easy Traditional 21g sachet
Maple syrup 2 tbsp
Sesame oil 1 tbsp
Sesame seeds 15-25g (½-1oz)
Pistachio nuts 25g (1oz), chopped
Chopped fresh mint to serve (optional)

1 Preheat oven to 200°C/180°fan/Gas 6. Cut aubergine into four slices, lengthways, then score the flesh in a criss-cross pattern. Place in a roasting tin in a single layer.
2 In a small bowl, mix together miso, maple syrup and sesame oil. Spoon two-thirds over aubergine slices. Bake for 10 minutes.
3 Turn up heat to 220°C/200°fan/Gas 7. Spoon remaining miso mixture over aubergine and sprinkle with sesame seeds and nuts. Bake for a further 10 minutes or until tender.
4 Scatter over mint to serve, if you like.
TIP Miso Easy Traditional sachets can be found in the Asian section in most large supermarkets. They can also be mixed with hot water to make warming miso soup.

Serves 2 as a starter or side • **Time 25 mins**
Calories 267 • Fibre 6g • Salt 1.1g • Sugar 8.5g
Fat 19.5g of which 2.9g is saturated

135

10 Monday

11 Tuesday

12 Wednesday

13 Thursday

14 Friday

REMINDERS

CHESTNUT MUSHROOM & THYME SOUP

Olive oil 1 tbsp
Leek 1 small, finely chopped
Celery 1 stick, finely chopped
Fresh thyme 2 sprigs, plus extra to serve
Chestnut mushrooms 250g (9oz), finely sliced
Vegetable stock pot or stock cube 1
Dried porcini mushrooms 1 tbsp, snipped into small pieces
Ciabatta loaf ½, cut into 6 diagonal slices
Crème fraîche 3 tbsp
Soft blue cheese 75g (3oz)

1 Heat oil in a large pan and cook leek, celery and thyme, covered, for 5 minutes until softened.
2 Add chestnut mushrooms, cook for a 2-3 minutes, then add stock pot (or crumble in stock cube) and pour over 600ml (1 pint) boiling water. Sprinkle dried mushrooms over, cover and simmer for 15 minutes.
3 Meanwhile, heat a griddle pan (or preheat grill) and toast ciabatta slices on both sides.
4 Remove thyme stalks, then whizz soup with a stick blender, adding 1 tablespoon of crème fraîche. Season to taste.
5 Spread blue cheese on toasts. Ladle soup into warmed bowls. Dot remaining crème fraîche on top of soup, season and sprinkle with extra thyme leaves.

Serves 2 • Time 30 mins
Calories 468 • Fibre 5.1g • Salt 1.1g • Sugar 8.5g
Fat 29.6g of which 15g is saturated

137

17 Monday

Don't forget to order your **2023 Dairy Diary**. Use the order form on page 170 or order online.
If you don't have a milkman, call 0344 4725265 or visit www.dairydiary.co.uk

☾ Last quarter

18 Tuesday

19 Wednesday

20 Thursday

21 Friday

REMINDERS

VEGAN SAUSAGE ROLLS

Dried mushrooms 40g (1½oz)
Sage and onion stuffing mix 50g (2oz)
Smoked firm tofu 150g (5oz), drained and grated
Sunflower oil 1 tbsp
Sweet chilli sauce 3 tbsp
Smoked paprika 2 tsp
Flax seeds (linseeds) 1 tsp, finely ground
Vegan ready-rolled puff pastry sheet 320g pack
Chia and sesame seeds 2 tsp each
Sweet chilli sauce or tomato ketchup to serve

1 Put mushrooms in a heatproof bowl and pour over 350ml (12fl oz) just-boiled water. Soak for 30 minutes then drain, squeezing out as much liquid as possible. Reserve the liquid. Chop mushrooms very finely.
2 Put stuffing mix in a bowl and mix in mushrooms and tofu. Heat 100ml (3½fl oz) soaking liquid with oil, chilli sauce and paprika until boiling, then stir into stuffing mixture. Leave to cool. Cover and chill until required.
3 Preheat oven to 200°C/180°fan/Gas 6. Line 2 baking trays with baking paper. Mix flax with 1 tbsp cold water to make a glaze.
4 Cut pastry sheet in half lengthways. Spoon half the filling along the middle of one of pastry lengths, shaping to form a sausage. Fold pastry over filling. Brush one edge with glaze and press together to seal. Repeat with remaining filling and pastry.
5 Turn rolls over so that the seam is underneath and cut each roll into 8. Arrange on baking trays, brush with glaze and sprinkle with seeds. Bake for 25 minutes until puffed and lightly golden. Best served warm with sweet chilli sauce or tomato ketchup to dip.

Makes 16 • **Time 45 mins plus soaking and cooling**
Calories 116 • Fibre 1g • Salt 0.4g • Sugar 0g
Fat 6.8g of which 2.8g is saturated

24 Monday

25 Tuesday
● New moon

26 Wednesday

27 Thursday

28 Friday

REMINDERS

Saturday 29
Don't forget to put your clocks back 1 hour tonight
(t.b.c. dependent on Government ruling)

Sunday 30

BLACK BEAN CHILLI

Olive oil 2 tbsp
Onions 2, peeled and chopped
Garlic 1 clove, peeled and grated
Red and yellow peppers 1 large of each
colour, deseeded and cut into chunks
Chipotle paste 1 tsp
Plum tomatoes 400g tin
Vegetable stock pot 1
Black beans 400g tin, drained and rinsed
Corn and wheat tortillas 2
Cheese 40g (1½oz), grated
Fresh coriander a good handful, torn
Pickled jalapeños a few (optional)

1 Heat 1 tablespoon oil and cook onions,
garlic and peppers over a low heat for
15 minutes.
2 Add paste, cook for a minute, then stir
in tomatoes, breaking up roughly with
a wooden spoon. Add stock pot, pour in
300ml (10fl oz) boiling water. Bring to boil
and simmer for 15-20 minutes. Add beans
and cook for 5 minutes until piping hot.
3 Meanwhile, preheat oven to 200°C/180°fan/
Gas 6. Using scissors, cut each tortilla into
12 triangles. Spread out on two large baking
sheets. Brush with remaining oil. Bake for
6-8 minutes until crispy and golden.
4 Spoon chilli into warm bowls, scatter with
cheese, coriander and jalapeños, if you like,
and serve with tortilla triangles.

Serves 2–3 • Time 45 mins
Calories 431 • Fibre 10.6g • Salt 1.4g • Sugar 5.1g
Fat 17.1g of which 5.5g is saturated

31 Monday
Halloween

1 Tuesday NOVEMBER
⟩ First quarter

2 Wednesday

3 Thursday

4 Friday

REMINDERS

Saturday 5

Bonfire Night

Sunday 6

GHOSTLY SWEET TREATS

Butter 200g (7oz), softened
Caster sugar 110g (4oz)
Medium eggs 2
Self-raising flour 110g (4oz)
Vanilla extract 1 tsp
Icing sugar 225g (8oz)
Seedless raspberry jam 12 heaped tsp
Edible eyes 24

1 Preheat oven to 180°C/160°fan/Gas 4. Put 12 fairy cake cases in a 12-hole muffin tray.
2 Beat 110g (4oz) butter with caster sugar until light and fluffy. Whisk in eggs one at a time, along with flour, half the vanilla, and 1 tablespoon water until smooth. Divide mix between cases. Bake for 20-25 minutes until risen and golden. Leave to cool completely on a wire rack.
3 Whisk remaining butter with icing sugar, remaining vanilla and 2 tablespoons warm water to make a spreadable buttercream.
4 Leaving a thin border, cut a cone shape out of each cake. Spoon jam into hole and place cone back on top, pointing upwards. Spread a heaped tablespoon of buttercream over each cake, creating a 'quiff' on top. Pop eyes on. The cakes will keep for a few days in an airtight container.
TIP If you're having trouble tracking down any edible eyes, try a specialist cake decoration shop or use currants instead.

Makes 12 • Time 55 mins plus cooling
Calories 306 • Fibre 0.5g • Salt 0.1g • Sugar 32.8g
Fat 14.9g of which 9.1g is saturated

143

7 Monday

8 Tuesday
○ Full moon

9 Wednesday

10 Thursday

11 Friday

REMINDERS

ASIAN-INSPIRED MASH WITH BANGERS

Sweet potato 1, peeled and roughly chopped
Pumpkin or butternut squash 500g (1lb 2oz), peeled and roughly chopped
Potato 1, peeled and roughly chopped
Butter 50g (2oz)
Soy sauce 3-4 tbsp
Spring onions 2-3, trimmed and finely sliced
Sesame seeds 1 tbsp, toasted
Sausages and cabbage wedges or broccoli to serve (optional)

1 Put sweet potato, squash and potato in a large pan, cover with water and bring to the boil. Reduce heat and simmer for 20 minutes until softened.
2 Drain vegetables well, then tip them back into pan. Dry over a high heat for 30 seconds, then add butter and soy sauce and mash until smooth. Season with freshly ground black pepper.
3 Stir in half the spring onions. Scatter mash with sesame seeds and remaining spring onions. Serve with sausages and cabbage wedges or broccoli, if you like.
TIP Use whichever veg you like – to a total weight of about 1kg (2lb 4oz).

Serves 6 • **Time 35 mins**
Calories 156 • Fibre 3.5g • Salt 1.1g • Sugar 0g
Fat 9g of which 4.7g is saturated

14 Monday

15 Tuesday

16 Wednesday
(Last quarter

17 Thursday

18 Friday

REMINDERS

HOG ROAST BUNS

Skin-on boneless pork leg joint 1.5kg (3lb 5oz)
Olive oil 4 tbsp
Dried sage 2 tsp
Eating apples 3, cored and thickly sliced
Large onion 1, peeled and thickly sliced
Sage and onion stuffing mix 125g (4½oz)
Bread rolls 8 large
Salad leaves a large handful
Apple sauce to serve

1 Heat oven to 240°C/220°fan/Gas 9. Remove any string from the pork. Mix 2 tablespoons oil with sage and seasoning and rub all over pork.
2 Put pork in a roasting tin and roast for 45 minutes to crisp up. Transfer pork to a plate. Reduce heat to 170°C/150°fan/Gas 3.
3 Put apples and onion in tin and mix into pan juices along with 4 tablespoons of water. Sit pork on top and roast for 3 hours, basting occasionally and topping up with water to prevent apples drying out, until pork is tender. Cover joint with foil if it browns too much. Lightly cover and rest for 30 minutes.
4 Meanwhile, make stuffing according to the packet instructions and leave to cool. Divide into 8 and flatten to make 1cm (½in) thick patties. Heat remaining oil in a frying pan and fry stuffing for 3-4 minutes each side until lightly golden. Drain and keep warm.
5 To serve, strip away skin and fat, then 'pull' meat into shreds. Chop apples and onions. Fill buns with salad, top with a stuffing patty, pork and the apple mixture. Cut up crispy skin and serve alongside, if you like. Accompany with apple sauce.

Makes 8 buns • Time 4 hrs plus resting
Calories 450 • Fibre 2.9g • Salt 1.2g • Sugar 1.2g
Fat 14.1g of which 3.7g is saturated

21 Monday

22 Tuesday

23 Wednesday
● New moon

24 Thursday

25 Friday

REMINDERS

SLOW-COOKED OXTAIL STEW

Plain flour 2 tbsp
Dried chilli flakes ½ tsp
Sweet smoked paprika 1 tbsp
Oxtail pieces 1.5kg (3lb 5oz)
Olive oil 2 tbsp
Carrots 450g (1lb), peeled and chopped
Red onions 2, peeled and sliced
Celery 2 sticks, sliced
Garlic 3 cloves, peeled and finely chopped
Red wine 300ml (½ pint)
Beef stock 300ml (½ pint)
Orange 1, finely grated zest and juice
Chopped tomatoes 400g tin
Light soft brown sugar 1 tbsp
Bay leaf 1
Fresh thyme a few sprigs
Cooked penne pasta to serve

1 Preheat oven to 150°C/130°fan/Gas 2. Mix flour and
1 teaspoon of salt and spices, then toss with oxtail.
2 Heat oil in a large frying pan and fry oxtail (reserving
leftover flour) for 5 minutes until browned all over.
Put the carrots in a large lidded casserole dish and
place oxtail pieces on top.
3 Reheat frying pan juices and gently fry onions,
celery and garlic for 5 minutes until softened. Stir in
reserved flour and add wine, stock and orange zest
and juice with tomatoes and sugar. Bring to the boil,
stirring, then pour over the oxtail.
4 Add bay and thyme, then cover and bake for 4½-5
hours until meat is falling off the bone. Discard bay
and thyme. Remove bones and spoon over pasta.

Serves 4 • Time 5½ hrs
Calories 817 • Fibre 8.8g • Salt 1.7g • Sugar 8.8g
Fat 38.1g of which 1.1g is saturated

149

28 Monday

29 Tuesday

30 Wednesday
) First quarter
St Andrew's Day

1 Thursday DECEMBER

2 Friday

REMINDERS

Saturday   3

Sunday   4

COCK-A-LEEKIE TRAY ROAST

Baby new potatoes 500g (1lb 2oz), halved if large
Carrot 1, peeled and cut into thick slices
Celery 2 stalks, roughly chopped
Bay leaves 2
Fresh thyme good handful of sprigs
Chicken thighs 8, trimmed of excess skin and fat
Olive oil 2 tbsp
Smoked bacon lardons 110g (4oz)
Butter 25g (1oz)
Leeks 2, trimmed and cut into thick slices
Stoned prunes 12

1 Preheat oven to 170°C/150°fan/Gas 3. Put potatoes
and carrot in a large pan, just cover with water and
bring to the boil for 5 minutes. Drain well, reserving
cooking water. Tip vegetables into a large roasting
tin, then add celery and herbs. Put chicken on top.
Pour in 500ml (18fl oz) cooking water. Drizzle with
oil, season well and roast for 40 minutes.
2 Cook lardons in a frying pan until browned but not
too crispy. Spoon out onto a plate. Add butter and
leeks to pan. Cover and cook over a low heat, stirring
occasionally for about 8 minutes until tender.
3 After 40 minutes, add leeks to roasting tin
along with bacon and prunes. Turn heat up to
190°C/170°fan/Gas 5. Cook for 20 minutes until
chicken is tender and juices run clear.
4 Spoon chicken and vegetables onto warmed plates.
Pour cooking juices into a pan and reduce over a high
heat. Serve in a jug alongside.
TIP You can use streaky bacon instead of lardons –
just cut each rasher into 4 strips.

Serves 4 • Time 1 hr 15 mins
Calories 487 • Fibre 5.2g • Salt 1.5g • Sugar 0g
Fat 30.5g of which 10g is saturated

151

5   Monday

6   Tuesday

7   Wednesday

8   Thursday
○ Full moon

9   Friday

Saturday 10

Sunday 11

SNOWY FESTIVE FIR TREES

Ready-rolled puff pastry sheet 320g pack
Milk 2 tsp
Mincemeat 275g (10oz)
Flaked almonds 2 tbsp
Icing sugar 75g (3oz), plus extra for dusting
Lemon juice 2 tsp

1 Unroll pastry and cut in half lengthways. Cut
9 triangles per strip, each 7cm (3in) across bottom
and about 12cm (5in) at sides. Reserve trimmings.
Arrange triangles on 2 baking trays lined with
baking paper. Score a line around triangles to make
a thin border. Cut small squares out of leftover
pastry and press onto base of each triangle for
a trunk. Brush border and trunk with milk. Chill.
Preheat oven to 200°C/180°fan/Gas 6.
2 Spoon a heaped teaspoon of mincemeat on each
triangle. Carefully spread inside border. Scatter
almonds over.
3 Bake for 20 minutes until crisp and golden. Leave
to cool on a wire rack.
4 Mix 75g (3oz) icing sugar with lemon juice and
1 teaspoon water. Drizzle icing at pointed end of
trees and a little further down to look like snow.
When set, dust with icing sugar.
TIPS Prepare one tray of trees and bake them while
you prepare the other tray. If the mincemeat slides
off trees while baking, quickly pile it back on as
soon as you take them out of the oven. These will
keep for three days in an airtight container.

Makes 18 • Time 1 hr 15 mins
Calories 137 • Fibre 0.9g • Salt 0.2g • Sugar 9g
Fat 6.3g of which 2.3g is saturated

153

12 Monday

13 Tuesday

14 Wednesday

15 Thursday

16 Friday
(Last quarter

REMINDERS

Saturday 17

Sunday 18

POLENTA & PARMESAN-CRUSTED ROOTS

Roasting potatoes 1kg (2lb 2oz)
Carrots 500g (1lb 2oz), peeled and cut into large chunks
Parsnips 500g (1lb 2oz), peeled and cut into large chunks
Olive oil 150ml (¼ pint)
Polenta 4 tbsp
Grated Parmesan 4 tbsp

1 Preheat oven to 220°C/200°fan/Gas 7. Peel potatoes thinly and cut into even-sized pieces, leaving small potatoes whole.
2 Put potatoes and carrots in a large saucepan of water, bring to the boil and cook for 3 minutes.
3 Add parsnips to the saucepan, bring back to the boil and cook for a further 2 minutes. Drain well and allow to dry off in a colander for 10 minutes.
4 Return vegetables to saucepan. Holding lid in place on saucepan, shake the pan several times to soften edges of vegetables. Carefully stir in 2 tablespoons of oil. Mix polenta and Parmesan with some seasoning and sprinkle over vegetables. Carefully mix to give a light coating.
5 Pour remaining oil into a large roasting tray and put in oven for 3-4 minutes until very hot. Carefully add vegetables, turning in the oil to coat them. Bake for 30-35 minutes, turning and basting occasionally, until crisp and golden. Drain and serve with a roast dinner.
TIP King Edward or Maris Piper are great for roasting.

Serves 6 • **Time 1 hr 10 mins plus drying**
Calories 478 • Fibre 10.3g • Salt 1.2g • Sugar 0g
Fat 29.4g of which 5.8g is saturated

19 Monday

20 Tuesday

21 Wednesday
Winter solstice
Winter begins

22 Thursday

23 Friday
● New moon

REMINDERS

Saturday 24
Christmas Eve

Sunday 25
Christmas Day

CHOCOLATE ORANGE PUD

Soft pitted dates 150g (5oz), finely chopped
Oranges 2, finely grated zest and juice
Unsalted butter 160g (5½oz), softened
Dark brown sugar 100g (3½oz)
Medium eggs 2, beaten
Mixed dried fruit 150g (5oz)
Self-raising flour 100g (3½oz)
Cocoa powder 25g (1oz)
Bicarbonate of soda 1 tsp
Dark chocolate 150g (5oz)
Double cream 100ml (3½fl oz)
Fresh orange segments to serve

1 Grease and line base of a 1 litre (1¾ pint) pudding basin. Put dates in a saucepan with half orange zest. Pour in half orange juice with 100ml (3½fl oz) water. Bring to boil, cover and simmer for 5 minutes until soft, pulpy, and liquid absorbed. Remove from heat, beat until smooth and leave to cool completely.
2 Whisk 110g (4oz) butter with sugar, date mixture and eggs until creamy. Stir in dried fruit then sift in flour, cocoa and bicarbonate of soda and fold together.
3 Spoon into basin and smooth top. Lay a round of baking parchment directly on top of mixture, then cover with foil with a pleat in the centre. Secure with string. Stand basin on a trivet in a large saucepan. Pour in water to come one-quarter of the way up the sides of the basin. Bring to boil, cover and steam for about 2½ hours until firm and a skewer inserted into the centre comes out clean. Leave to stand for 10 minutes.

Serves 8 • Time 3 hrs plus cooling and standing
Calories 534 • Fibre 3.2g • Salt 0.6g • Sugar 25.4g
Fat 21g of which 18.9g is saturated

4 For the sauce, break chocolate into a saucepan and add remaining butter, orange zest and juice. Heat very gently until melted. Remove from heat and stir in cream. Serve with pudding and fresh orange segments.

26 Monday
Boxing Day
Bank Holiday, UK

27 Tuesday
Bank Holiday, UK

28 Wednesday

29 Thursday

30 Friday
⟩ First quarter

REMINDERS

Saturday 31
New Year's Eve

JANUARY 2023 **Sunday** 1
New Year's Day

BOMBAY SPICED NUTS

Mixed unsalted nuts 400g (14oz)
Ghee 2 tbsp
Sea salt flakes 1 tbsp
Ground cumin 2 tsp
Ground coriander 2 tsp
Chilli powder 1 tsp

1 Preheat oven to 180°C/160°fan/Gas 4.
Spread nuts out in a shallow roasting tin and
roast for 10-12 minutes until golden all over,
shaking occasionally.
2 Melt ghee in a small frying pan and when
hot, add the salt and spices. Fry for 30-60
seconds until fragrant, taking care not to
burn. Pour spicy ghee over nuts in tin and
mix in well. Spread out on a cold tray to cool.
3 Store nuts in an airtight container for a few
days. They can be put into bags or wrapped
in paper to give as gifts. They will keep for
up to a week.
TIPS Skin-on almonds, pistachios and
cashews work best for this recipe. Freshly
ground spices (in a pestle and mortar) won't
stick as well to the nuts so use ready-ground
spices. Ghee is less likely to burn than butter.
If you don't want to buy a tin of it, use
vegetable oil and a bit of butter for flavour,
but watch it does not burn.

Serves 12 • **Time 15 mins**
Calories 216 • Fibre 0.4g • Salt 1.2g • Sugar 0g
Fat 19.1g of which 4.1g is saturated

159

2 Monday
Bank Holiday, UK

3 Tuesday
Bank Holiday, Scotland

4 Wednesday

5 Thursday

6 Friday
○ Full moon

REMINDERS

NOTES

NOTES

NOTES

NOTES

Three ways to order your Dairy Diary

FROM YOUR MILKMAN
Use the **order form overleaf**, or, if you usually order via your dairy's website, please order online.

TELEPHONE
If you do not have a milkman, call **0344 4725265.**
Your diary will be posted to you.

ONLINE
Visit **dairydiary.co.uk**
See full details of the 2023 Dairy Diary and other great products.

Reserve your Dairy Diary 2023

To reserve your copy of the 2023 Dairy Diary, please fill in the form overleaf and leave it out with your empties from September onwards.

If you usually order via your dairy's website, please order online.

Order form overleaf...

Dairy Diary 2023

Order form

MILKMAN PLEASE LEAVE ME

☐ copies of the **Dairy Diary 2023**

☐ copies of the **Dairy Diary Set**

Name

Address

Postcode

THANK YOU

Please leave out for your milkman from September 2022 onwards

---

RECIPE NOTES

- Nutritional information has been calculated by portion or item. Where there are portion variations, e.g. serves 6–8, the analysis given is based on the larger number.
- Spoon measures are level unless otherwise stated.
- Eggs are large unless otherwise stated.
- Sugar is 'free sugars' (added sugars, including those naturally present in fruit juice, honey & syrups, but excluding the natural sugars present in all fruit and vegetables).
- Recipes that do not contain animal products (such as meat, fish, poultry, dairy, eggs and honey) are suitable for vegans. Please check ingredients carefully for dietary suitability.

SAFETY NOTES

- Recipes using nuts or nut products are not suitable for young children or those with a nut allergy.
- Certain at-risk groups, such as pregnant women, babies and sick or elderly people should not eat raw or lightly cooked eggs.

V Suitable for vegetarians, provided a suitable cheese, yogurt or pesto etc. is used.

Ⓥ Suitable for vegans provided the non-dairy options are chosen, and no honey is added.

F Suitable for freezing.

RECITE INDEX

THERE ARE LOTS MORE RECIPES AT

DAIRYDIARY.CO.UK

PLANNER 2023

JANUARY	FEBRUARY	MARCH
1 Sun	1 Wed	1 Wed
2 Mon BANK HOLIDAY UK	2 Thu	2 Thu
3 Tue BANK HOLIDAY SCOTLAND	3 Fri	3 Fri
4 Wed	**4 Sat**	**4 Sat**
5 Thu	**5 Sun**	**5 Sun**
6 Fri	6 Mon	6 Mon
7 Sat	7 Tue	7 Tue
8 Sun	8 Wed	8 Wed
9 Mon	9 Thu	9 Thu
10 Tue	10 Fri	10 Fri
11 Wed	**11 Sat**	**11 Sat**
12 Thu	**12 Sun**	**12 Sun**
13 Fri	13 Mon	13 Mon
14 Sat	14 Tue	14 Tue
15 Sun	15 Wed	15 Wed
16 Mon	16 Thu	16 Thu
17 Tue	17 Fri	17 Fri BANK HOLIDAY N. IRELAND
18 Wed	**18 Sat**	**18 Sat**
19 Thu	**19 Sun**	**19 Sun**
20 Fri	20 Mon	20 Mon
21 Sat	21 Tue	21 Tue
22 Sun	22 Wed	22 Wed
23 Mon	23 Thu	23 Thu
24 Tue	24 Fri	24 Fri
25 Wed	**25 Sat**	**25 Sat**
26 Thu	**26 Sun**	**26 Sun**
27 Fri	27 Mon	27 Mon
28 Sat	28 Tue	28 Tue
29 Sun		29 Wed
30 Mon		30 Thu
31 Tue		31 Fri

APRIL		MAY		JUNE	
1	**Sat**	1	Mon · BANK HOLIDAY UK	1	Thu
2	**Sun**	2	Tue	2	Fri
3	Mon	3	Wed	**3**	**Sat**
4	Tue	4	Thu	**4**	**Sun**
5	Wed	5	Fri	5	Mon
6	Thu	**6**	**Sat**	6	Tue
7	Fri · BANK HOLIDAY UK	**7**	**Sun**	7	Wed
8	**Sat**	8	Mon	8	Thu
9	**Sun**	9	Tue	9	Fri
10	Mon · BANK HOLIDAY UK (EXCL. SCOTLAND)	10	Wed	**10**	**Sat**
11	Tue	11	Thu	**11**	**Sun**
12	Wed	12	Fri	12	Mon
13	Thu	**13**	**Sat**	13	Tue
14	Fri	**14**	**Sun**	14	Wed
15	**Sat**	15	Mon	15	Thu
16	**Sun**	16	Tue	16	Fri
17	Mon	17	Wed	**17**	**Sat**
18	Tue	18	Thu	**18**	**Sun**
19	Wed	19	Fri	19	Mon
20	Thu	**20**	**Sat**	20	Tue
21	Fri	**21**	**Sun**	21	Wed
22	**Sat**	22	Mon	22	Thu
23	**Sun**	23	Tue	23	Fri
24	Mon	24	Wed	**24**	**Sat**
25	Tue	25	Thu	**25**	**Sun**
26	Wed	26	Fri	26	Mon
27	Thu	**27**	**Sat**	27	Tue
28	Fri	**28**	**Sun**	28	Wed
29	**Sat**	29	Mon · BANK HOLIDAY UK	29	Thu
30	**Sun**	30	Tue	30	Fri
		31	Wed		P.T.O. July–December 2023

PLANNER 2023

JULY		AUGUST		SEPTEMBER	
1	**Sat**	1	Tue	1	Fri
2	**Sun**	2	Wed	**2**	**Sat**
3	Mon	3	Thu	**3**	**Sun**
4	Tue	4	Fri	4	Mon
5	Wed	**5**	**Sat**	5	Tue
6	Thu	**6**	**Sun**	6	Wed
7	Fri	7	Mon BANK HOLIDAY SCOTLAND	7	Thu
8	**Sat**	8	Tue	8	Fri
9	**Sun**	9	Wed	**9**	**Sat**
10	Mon	10	Thu	**10**	**Sun**
11	Tue	11	Fri	11	Mon
12	Wed BANK HOLIDAY N. IRELAND	**12**	**Sat**	12	Tue
13	Thu	**13**	**Sun**	13	Wed
14	Fri	14	Mon	14	Thu
15	**Sat**	15	Tue	15	Fri
16	**Sun**	16	Wed	**16**	**Sat**
17	Mon	17	Thu	**17**	**Sun**
18	Tue	18	Fri	18	Mon
19	Wed	**19**	**Sat**	19	Tue
20	Thu	**20**	**Sun**	20	Wed
21	Fri	21	Mon	21	Thu
22	**Sat**	22	Tue	22	Fri
23	**Sun**	23	Wed	**23**	**Sat**
24	Mon	24	Thu	**24**	**Sun**
25	Tue	25	Fri	25	Mon
26	Wed	**26**	**Sat**	26	Tue
27	Thu	**27**	**Sun**	27	Wed
28	Fri	28	Mon BANK HOLIDAY UK (EXCL. SCOTLAND)	28	Thu
29	**Sat**	29	Tue	29	Fri
30	**Sun**	30	Wed	**30**	**Sat**
31	Mon	31	Thu		

OCTOBER	NOVEMBER	DECEMBER
1 Sun	1 Wed	1 Fri
2 Mon	2 Thu	**2 Sat**
3 Tue	3 Fri	**3 Sun**
4 Wed	**4 Sat**	4 Mon
5 Thu	**5 Sun**	5 Tue
6 Fri	6 Mon	6 Wed
7 Sat	7 Tue	7 Thu
8 Sun	8 Wed	8 Fri
9 Mon	9 Thu	**9 Sat**
10 Tue	10 Fri	**10 Sun**
11 Wed	**11 Sat**	11 Mon
12 Thu	**12 Sun**	12 Tue
13 Fri	13 Mon	13 Wed
14 Sat	14 Tue	14 Thu
15 Sun	15 Wed	15 Fri
16 Mon	16 Thu	**16 Sat**
17 Tue	17 Fri	**17 Sun**
18 Wed	**18 Sat**	18 Mon
19 Thu	**19 Sun**	19 Tue
20 Fri	20 Mon	20 Wed
21 Sat	21 Tue	21 Thu
22 Sun	22 Wed	22 Fri
23 Mon	23 Thu	**23 Sat**
24 Tue	24 Fri	**24 Sun**
25 Wed	**25 Sat**	25 Mon BANK HOLIDAY UK
26 Thu	**26 Sun**	26 Tue BANK HOLIDAY UK
27 Fri	27 Mon	27 Wed
28 Sat	28 Tue	28 Thu
29 Sun	29 Wed	29 Fri
30 Mon	30 Thu	**30 Sat**
31 Tue		**31 Sun**

ACKNOWLEDGEMENTS

Managing Editor
Emily Davenport

Author/Editor
Louise Burfitt

Art Editor
Graham Meigh

Production
Siobhan Hennessey

Recipes
Emily Davenport
Kathryn Hawkins
Kate Moseley

Photographer
Steve Lee

Food Stylist
Sian Davies

Props Stylist
Olivia Wardle

Recipe Testing
Emily Bagshaw
Sam Crompton
Lucy Goodman

Nutritional Analysis
Paul McArdle

Proofreader
Aune Butt

Brand Manager
Emma Snow

Special Thanks

Alaska Seafood Marketing Institute
Denise Spencer-Walker
Pam Lloyd
Seafish
Simply Beef & Lamb

In fond memory of Kate Moseley, who
provided us with so many wonderful recipes.

MIX
Paper from
responsible sources
FSC® C020056
www.fsc.org

Published by Eaglemoss Ltd

Barn 3, Somerford Business Court, Somerford, Congleton, CW12 4SN

Dairy Diary orders telephone: 0344 4725265

Editorial queries telephone: 01270 270050

Website: dairydiary.co.uk   Facebook: @DairyDiary   Instagram: @OriginalDairyDiary

Email: enquiries@dairydiary.co.uk

While every care has been taken in compiling the information in this Diary, the publishers cannot accept responsibility for any errors, inadvertent or not, that may be found or may occur at some time in future owing to changes in legislation or any other reason. © Eaglemoss Ltd 2021/2022

PICTURE CREDITS

Cover Shutterstock/djgis; 21 Shutterstock/Hannamariah; 22 Alamy; 23 Shutterstock/chrisdorney; 23 Shutterstock/wavebreakmedia; 26 Shutterstock/Daria_Cherry; 27 Shutterstocl/LightField Studios; 20 Max Pixel; 31 Shutterstock/Babkina Svetlana; 32 Shutterstock/Monkey Business Images; 33 Shutterstock/ESB Professional; 34 Shutterstock/Daisy Daisy; 35 Shutterstock/Dusan Petkovic; 35 Shutterstocl/Sriyana; 37 Shutterstock/Bringolo; 37 Shutterstock/Manuel Trinidad Mesa; 38 Shutterstock/Kaprisova; 39 Shutterstock/patjo; 40 Shutterstock/Laurence Lynch; 41 Shutterstock/Dragana Gordic; 42 Shutterstock/Oksana Mizina; 42 Shutterstock/Simon Booth; 43 Shutterstock/Simon Booth; 46 Pixabay/sansoja; 50 Max Pixel; 55-159 Eaglemoss/Steve Lee except 67, 81, 93 simplybeefandlamb.co.uk; 103 fishisthedish.co.uk; 101 britishasparagus.com; 109, 117 Alaska Seafood Marketing Institute; 123 lovecelery.co.uk; 127 loveradish.co.uk